DATE DUE

FACULTY ITEM DUE END OF SPRING SEMESTER		

Demco No. 62-0549

THE WORLD'S GREAT BRIDGES

THE WORLD'S
GREAT BRIDGES

By H. Shirley Smith

O.B.E., M. Inst. C.E., M. Am. Soc. C.E.,
D.I.C., B. Sc., A.C.G.I.

With 24 Line Drawings
By Rowland J. Mainstone, M. Eng.
and 43 Photo Plates

75018

HARPER & ROW, PUBLISHERS
NEW YORK AND EVANSTON

DEDICATED

to the late Sir Ralph Freeman, 1880-
1950, Consulting Engineer of London,
designer of Sydney Harbour bridge, and
worthy upholder of the great traditions
of bridge builders, handed down by men
such as Telford, Robert Stephenson,
Brunel, and Benjamin Baker

Library of Congress catalog card number: 54-8993

Foreword

THIS BOOK has been written for all those interested in bridges, whether young or old, engineers or laymen.

The word 'great' has been interpreted in its widest sense to include bridges distinguished in their conception and design, those which advanced the science of bridge-building, those in which the most formidable difficulties were overcome during construction, and last but not least the mighty spans of to-day.

The building of a big bridge confers a rare sense of achievement, one might almost say elation, on the engineers responsible. Standing on the bank of the river, and looking over the broad brimming width to be bridged, one feels extraordinarily insignificant in the face of its challenge and the unknown obstacles which may well be encountered. I have tried here to impart something of the thrill of achievement as one by one the difficulties emerge and are overcome, and slowly the bridge takes shape, the piers rise above the water, and the spans stretch out from shore to shore.

I have made what I believe to be the first attempt in a book of this kind to assess the work of British bridge-builders, not only in the Empire but in all countries overseas, and to show what these anonymous engineers achieved with untrained labour, and the simplest plant and tools, in the face of all the forces that Nature put against them.

But the tale is not unchequered; it is not all of triumph; it includes disasters such as those that befell the first Tay bridge and the bridges at Quebec and Tacoma Narrows. Besides telling the story of these defeats, I have tried to unravel the causes behind them and to set down the lessons they taught us.

No one, alas, can have seen all the world's great bridges; but it has been my good fortune to visit the majority of those that are standing, and to work on the design or erection of the longest single spans in India, Africa, and Australia.

In the investigation that was needed, particularly in research both here and on the Continent for the first five chapters, I am indebted to Mr Rowland J. Mainstone, M.Eng. for his unflagging interest and industry. I was delighted when he agreed also to make the drawings which illustrate the text.

Unless there is any significance in the odd inches, dimensions are generally stated to the nearest foot. Every attempt has been made to check the facts, but if there are any errors, I am afraid I must accept responsibility.

Bridge engineers amongst my friends, who have between them read all the chapters and given valuable criticism and advice, include Mr E. Bateson, M.Inst.C.E.; Mr Ralph Freeman, C.B.E., M.Inst.C.E.; Mr O. A. Kerensky, B.Sc., M.Inst.C.E.; and Mr E. O. Measor, B.Sc., M.Inst.C.E. To all of these, to my Publishers for their invaluable and constructive criticism, and to many others who have assisted in innumerable ways I give my grateful thanks.

London,
February, 1953.

Contents

Acknowledgments

The author and publishers gratefully acknowledge permission to reproduce photographs to the following: the Spanish State Tourist Board, Plate 1; the French Government Tourist Office, New York, 2 and 3; the Trustees of the British Museum, 4; the Italian State Tourist Office, 5; British Railways, 6 and 7; Mr. G. A. Maunsell, 8 and 12; Messrs. Dorman Long & Co., 13, 27, 31, and 32; the Commissioner of Railways, New South Wales, 14; Messrs. Rendel Palmer & Tritton, 15; the Cleveland Bridge Co., Darlington, 16, 28, 29, and 30; the Cement & Concrete Association and Mr. Max Bill, 17; Mr. Max Bill, 18; Messrs. Peter Lind & Co., Ltd., 19; M. I. Haggbom, Skanska Cement Co., 20 and 21; the Dominion Bridge Co., Ltd., Canada, 23 and 24; the Pre-Stressed Concrete Co., Ltd., 25; the Bethlehem Steel Co., 26; the California Division of Highways, 33, 34, 35, and 36; Mr. O. H. Ammann, 37 and 38; Prof. F. B. Farquharson, University of Washington, 39, 40, and 41; the Golden Gate Bridge & Highway District, 1938, 42 and 43.

Also permission to reproduce the extract from *A Land* by Jacquetta Hawkes published by Random House, and the extract from "The Dry Salvages" in *Four Quartets,* copyright, 1943, by T. S. Eliot. Used by permission of Harcourt, Brace & Company.

List of Illustrations

The photographic plates will be found following page 52

List of Illustrations

Chapter 1

THE BEGINNINGS

I do not know much about Gods, but I think that the river
Is a strong brown God—sullen, untamed, and intractable,
Patient to some degree, at first recognized as a frontier;
Useful, untrustworthy as a conveyor of commerce;
Then only a problem confronting the builder of bridges.

T. S. ELIOT, *The Dry Salvages*

THE FIRST man-made bridge was probably a tree trunk or flat
stone laid across a stream. No doubt it was made many thousands
of years before the birth of Christ. Even before that, primitive
man must have wondered at natural arches such as the Pont d'Arc
at Ardèche that has a span of 194 feet rising 111 feet over the
river. But ages would have passed before some pioneer jammed
two stones together like an inverted 'V' across a narrow brook and
so built the first arch bridge.

We can only speculate on these beginnings. We see primitive
suspension bridges made of twisted creepers or lianas tied to tree
trunks on either side of a gorge and spanning it like a perilously
hung cobweb. But when these bridges were evolved or which
came first we cannot say with certainty. We only know that the
three types, beam or girder bridges (typified by a tree trunk
across a stream), arch bridges, and suspension bridges, have been
known and built from the earliest times of which we have any
record. In their simplest form beam or girder bridges are called
simple spans; if two or more are joined together over the piers
they become continuous; or they may be built as described on
page 6 to form cantilever bridges. These, however, are only
varieties of girder bridges and do not constitute a different type.
The three types, girder, arch, and suspension, may be varied or
combined to assist each other in the same structure; and down
the years materials of construction have evolved from those
ready to hand, such as timber and stone, to manufactured
materials such as brick, concrete, iron, and steel.

What is the difference between these types? The answer is illustrated in Fig. 1. The foundations of all three kinds, of course, have to support the weight of the bridge and the traffic on it; but arch and suspension bridges call on the ground to do more than this. An arch bridge thrusts outwards on its abutments. This explains the meaning of the proverb, 'An arch never sleeps'; the weight of the bridge, by virtue of its arch formation, is always tending to thrust the abutments outwards. Conversely, the cable of a suspension bridge pulls on its anchorage—whether it be the tree round which the creepers have been tied, or the

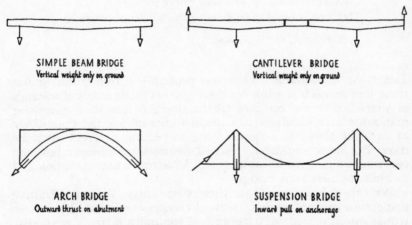

SIMPLE BEAM BRIDGE
Vertical weight only on ground

CANTILEVER BRIDGE
Vertical weight only on ground

ARCH BRIDGE
Outward thrust on abutment

SUSPENSION BRIDGE
Inward pull on anchorage

FIG. 1. The main types of bridge. The arrows indicate the directions of the forces on the ground.

mighty structure of concrete and steel which anchors the cables of the huge spans of to-day. Thus an arch is always in a state of compression and thrusting outwards; and a suspension bridge cable is in tension and tends to pulls its anchorages inwards. Both these types rely on the ground to resist a horizontal force. Beams or girder bridges in all their varieties are the exception. They are self-contained; they simply rest on the ground and exert no horizontal reaction on it.

A comparatively modern variant is to be found in tied-arch and self-anchored suspension bridges. In a tied arch, a horizontal tie is built to connect the ends of the arch and carry the horizontal thrust that would otherwise act on the abutments. In a self-anchored suspension bridge, a strut is built, usually at deck level, between the two anchorages, which relieves them of any horizontal pull.

The simplest examples of the first type are the 'clam' bridges of South-East Cornwall and the 'clapper' bridges of Dartmoor. 'Clam' is an Anglo-Saxon word meaning a twig or stick and denotes a tree trunk bridge; 'clapper' means a natural bridge or stepping-stones. Clam bridges were made in Cornwall where timber was easier to get than stone; but on Dartmoor, where slabs of moor-stone outcrop on the surface, huge flat boulders were used and we find the famous clapper bridges. Postbridge over the East Dart has three openings of 15 feet spanned by unchiselled slabs of granite 6 feet wide on piers of piled-up stone. It has been suggested that these bridges may have been contemporary with the dolmen, or stone bee-hive hut, which was built of unworked stones in pre-historic times. Their piers resemble menhirs and their slabs the horizontal beam of a cromlech or stonehenge. It seems improb-able, however, as most of the rivers they span are fordable, that these bridges would have been built at a time as primitive as the Bronze Age. Primitive man and his sheep or cattle would surely have splashed through the streams at the fords. It appears more likely that the clapper bridges, although they resemble dolmens, are the product of a more civilized period and no earlier than the late Middle Ages. They are not confined to Dartmoor, however; bridges of the same kind are found in Spain and there is evidence that they were used in Egypt, Babylon, and China.

According to Degrand, the earliest bridge on record is that built on the Nile by Menes, the first King of the Egyptians, about 2650 B.C.; but no details are forthcoming. A detailed description of another bridge built about five centuries later is given by Diodorus Siculus—the fabulous bridge built by Semiramis, Queen of Babylon, over the Euphrates. Herodotus ascribes this bridge to Queen Nitocris who ruled five generations later. First the river was diverted well above the city into an artificial lake, so that the piers of the bridge could be built in the dry in the river bed. The stones of the piers were bonded together by iron bars soldered in with lead. The deck was of timber, cedar, cypress, and palm, and was no less than 30 feet wide; part of it was removable and was taken up each night to afford protection from robbers. When the bridge was finished the river was brought back into its original channel. So the record reads to-day; how much is true and how much due to embellishment through the ages we shall never know; but there is no doubt that a remarkable bridge was built 4,000 years ago in Babylon.

*   *   *

How were rivers diverted in order to build the early bridges? One way was doubtless to select a site at an elbow or bend of the river and to cut a channel through the neck of the peninsula at the same time damming off the flow in the old channel. Another and probably later method may have been to divert the river first to one half of its channel and then to the other. This could be done by driving a double row of timber piles out from the river bank and filling up the space between them with clay or chalk to make a more or less watertight wall; lines of piles driven thus side by side and touching one another are called 'sheet' piles. After draining out the water from the enclosed area the bridge piers could then be built in the dry. It seems very doubtful, however, whether rivers could have been successfully diverted in those days, unless the flow was seasonal and reduced to a trickle in dry weather. It is perhaps significant that none of the references to this procedure was made at the time of its supposed use.

In countries where little stone was available but forests were abundant, foundations were made on timber piles. No doubt the earliest use of these was in the dwellings of lake villages, where piles were used as bearers to support the buildings. The primitive method of driving such piles by means of a cylindrical stone with handles can still be seen in the Far East. A number of men stand on a platform fixed below the head of the pile and ram the stone lustily up and down on top of it. This is usually done in tune to a rude, improvised chant concerning the passers-by, all the men joining in the chorus.

In later years piles were employed as bearers to give support beneath bridge piers in soft ground. After driving, the heads of all the piles were cut off to the same level at the bottom of the excavation; a timber platform, or grillage[1], was then placed on top of the piles and the piers built up stone by stone on the timber platform. Alternatively piles were used as in Caesar's bridge over the Rhine, in which they projected well above the surface of the water and formed trestles which served as bridge piers.

The next development was probably the driving of four rows of timber sheet piles to make a box, open of course at the top and bottom, completely surrounding the site of the proposed pier.

[1] A construction of cross-beams

Such a box is called a cofferdam and it may possibly have evolved from the use of walls of piling driven to divert a river. The earliest cofferdams no doubt simply served the purpose of containing stones and mortar deposited through the water inside them. At a later date engineers discovered how to empty the cofferdam, so that they could excavate the river bed as necessary and build the pier inside the enclosure in the dry. This could not, of course, be done until they had discovered methods of making the cofferdam reasonably watertight and some means, such as water wheels or scoops, for removing the water inside it. The Romans are the first bridge builders of whom we have any record who systematically used cofferdams on a large scale. As we shall see, however, the method was known and used in China, though with other materials, 2,000 years ago.

In countries such as Persia, where over large tracts of desert little if any timber was available, the use of cofferdams was unknown. The only ways of making bridge piers in such conditions were:

(*a*) To rely for the foundations on a wide mound of stones dropped through the water, in the hope that they would consolidate on the river bed.

(*b*) To divert the river in the dry season.

(*c*) To select a site where outcrops of rock were available, somewhat like stepping-stones, right across the river, and to build the piers on these.

The adoption of the last of these alternatives led, as we shall see, to some distinctive developments in Persian bridges.

In localities where both stone and timber were available, both were used. Bridge piers were then sometimes built of logs laid criss-cross, and resting on a foundation of stones, as in the bridges at Srinagar.

*   *   *

The practice of human sacrifice in the foundations of a bridge to placate the river gods appears to have prevailed from the earliest times up to the days of the Roman Republic. Offended because the bridge deprived them of their legitimate toll of human life, the gods must be appeased, otherwise they would provoke catastrophes to hinder its completion. It was possibly some form of this folk tale that gave rise to the Faust legend, which is encountered all over Europe and is responsible for the numerous

Devil's bridges which are to be found. The construction of the bridge is begun but the work is delayed by disaster. The river gods must be propitiated; the master builder in despair invokes the devil to help him; the devil promises aid on condition that he can secure a soul as payment—here we see the remains of the sacrificial-atonement idea; maybe the devil wins, but usually the bridge-builder manages to outwit him; virtue triumphs over evil, the devil is defeated, and Christianity triumphant.

*   *   *

A development of the girder bridge to enable it to be used for longer spans is known as a cantilever bridge (Fig. 1). A cantilever

FIG. 2. A primitive cantilever bridge over the river Jhelum at Srinagar. The roadway is lined with shops.

is essentially a bracket that juts out. A cantilever bridge is made up of two such brackets, or arms, which stand on the piers of the bridge and jut out towards each other from opposite sides of the river. Each of them is counter-balanced or tied back to an anchorage behind the pier; the two ends in the middle are joined by a short simple span. The earliest cantilever bridges were made wholly of timber and many in remote parts of the world still are. Some of the most picturesque are those over the river Jhelum at Srinagar, the capital of Kashmir (Fig. 2). Piles were driven and old boats filled with stones sunk at the site of the piers until a height above low water level was reached. Then the piers were built of rough-hewn deodar logs piled criss-cross, from the forests in the vicinity; the logs in each successive row stretching across the river were cut longer than those in the row immediately beneath, so that the logs on two adjacent piers jut further out towards each other as the height increases; the two ends are finally joined below roadway level by long tree trunks placed across the gap. The skeleton piers of these bridges have weathered many a severe flood, as they offer less resistance than would a solid pier to the volume of water that comes down as the river rises.

Bamboos lashed together are still often used in the construction of primitive cantilever bridges. Turner[1], in his account of his embassy to Tibet, described a bridge he discovered at Wandipore in Bhutan that was built entirely of turpentine fir joined together by wooden pegs. So far as he could see no metal of any kind had been used. Both the bridge and the castle nearby, with its gilded canopy, were said to have been built by Lam Sobroo in the seventeenth century. The bridge had three gateways, one at each end and one on a pier in midstream. The greater of its two spans measured 112 feet and was divided almost equally into two cantilever arms and a suspended span. In Norway, cantilever bridges were built of tall timber masts or poles, laid horizontally in tiers somewhat like the bridges in Kashmir. Passengers are said to have been so alarmed by the swaying of these bridges that they always dismounted and led their horses over.

*　　*　　*

Arch construction appears to have originated in the ancient cities between the Tigris and Euphrates, where the secret was held not less than 2,000 years before the Roman Conquest. Some of the earlier arches, whether built of stone or brick, were constructed in horizontal courses, each succeeding stone being corbelled out beyond the one below it. They were found widely distributed over the world, particularly in the Middle East, Mexico, and China, and may have developed from forms of stone cantilevers. The first arches built with voussoirs (i.e. tapered or wedge-shaped stones), were discovered in ancient Egyptian monuments. It is not known which type of construction came first. An elliptical arch built in brick with joints normal to the surface was found in the tomb of Amenophis I and must therefore date from eighteen centuries B.C. The commonest form of arch found in Persia was the ogival, or pointed, arch, although the Persians also used the elliptical form. The first users of the semi-circular arch, built with voussoirs

[1] Lt. Samuel Turner, *An Account of an Embassy to the Court of the Tashoo Lama in Tibet*, 1800.

erected on timber centering[1], or staging, appear to have been the Etruscans, in Central Italy.

After the Roman Conquest, the new rulers absorbed the culture and to some extent the customs of the peoples they had overrun, at the same time contributing their own brand of utilitarian and practical thought. They adopted the Etruscan semi-circular arch, modified according to the Roman idea, and during the five centuries of their supremacy introduced it over the whole of the Western world.

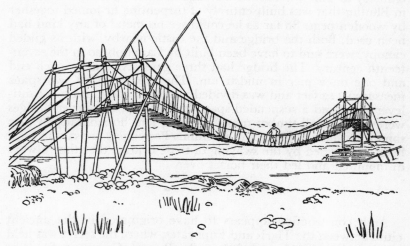

FIG. 3. A primitive suspension bridge made of saplings and twisted liana, and crossing the Salween river in southern China.

In the Far East, however, China remained aloof and unknown. As we shall see in a later chapter the type of arch bridge evolved there was of an entirely different kind.

*　　*　　*

Perhaps the simplest of all the primitive types of bridge are the earliest 'one-way-at-a-time' suspension bridges. These consist of a single cable; the unfortunate traveller sits in a loop which passes over the cable and pulls himself along; or he may sit in comparative comfort in a basket and be hauled across by others

[1] A temporary framework on which an arch is supported during its construction.

on the opposite bank. In a bridge over the Brahmaputra, Barber[1] noted that the cable was made of three strands of bamboo rope, each one inch thick, twisted together and spanning 600 feet. A more alarming development was the two-way bridge of similar kind, in which a cable is provided for travel in each direction and slopes down so that the traveller slides along under his own weight. The wooden slides are grooved and well greased with substances like yak butter, to reduce friction, but even so the cables have to be frequently renewed. Kingdon Ward refers to the heat generated by friction and the practice in Yunnan for the traveller to lubricate and cool the rope by trickling water on to it from a bamboo tube as he makes the crossing. In the third type, which is a true bridge, a walkway of some kind is provided for the traveller. Sometimes the bridge is supported by three cables; then the two on either side act as handrails and the passenger walks on the third which is tied below. Bridges of this kind are commonly found in China, India, Africa, and South America (Fig. 3). When the bridges are built, the cables are towed or floated across the river, hauled up and anchored to posts set in the ground, or are tied round large trees. A wide variety of materials including cane, bamboo, birch, vines, twisted lianas or creepers, and ox-hide thongs is used. These bridges have one attribute in common; they all sway and sag so alarmingly in use that it is said that nervous passengers have had to be blindfolded, tied to a stretcher, and carried across.

In South America, mules are slung across the rivers, kicking and plunging in two girths round the belly and the neck, which slide along a pair of 'tarabitas'—ropes up to 6 or 8 inches thick, made of twisted ox-hide thongs. In Sikkim, canes $\frac{3}{4}$ inch thick and 20 or 30 yards long, from a species of calamus, are knotted together to form the cables, and the floor is made of loose bamboos suspended below. A Lepcha carrying 140 lb. on his back will cross a torrent on such a bridge, steadily and with complete confidence.

* * *

The last variety of primitive bridge to which we must refer is the bridge of boats. This of course is simply a girder type of bridge on floating supports. The idea may have originated through the lashing together of a few boats to maintain a river

[1] E. C. Barber, *A Journey of Exploration in Western Szechuan*, Royal Geographical Society Supplementary Papers, Vol. II, 1881.

crossing, either to meet a special need or when the stream had dwindled and was narrow. Considerable resources were needed to build a pontoon bridge of substantial size and, as might be expected, we first encounter it in a military campaign. Herodotus tells how in 481 B.C. the Phoenicians and Egyptians had constructed bridges across the Hellespont at Abydos for the passage of the army of Xerxes, King of Persia, in his expedition against Greece. Much to the wrath of the king the bridges were destroyed in a violent gale. After ordering the waters to be chastised, rebuked, and branded, Xerxes instructed his engineers to build two more bridges. They gathered 674 vessels, penteconters and triremes[1], tying them together by means of ropes and securing them with long anchors. For the main cables, two ropes of white flax were used and four of papyrus. On top of these, sawn tree trunks were fastened transversely, and a roadway of earth rammed down on a foundation of brushwood.

After offering up prayers, Xerxes threw his cup into the straits and a golden bowl and a Persian sword—possibly as an offering to the sun, or possibly as a form of appeasement to the sea for having scourged and upbraided the waves. However that may be, the army then crossed on its way to the subjugation of Europe. Ten thousand Persians led the van, then a host of horsemen and spearmen of all nations. Such was the multitude that it took seven days and nights to cross without halting at all. Since that date many pontoon bridges have been built; but their maintenance is heavy, their life short, and they are more suitable for temporary than for permanent crossings.

---

[1] Penteconter, a Greek ship having fifty oars.   Trireme, a galley with three banks of oars.

Chapter 2

ROMAN BRIDGES

When we build, let it be such a work as our
descendants will thank us for; and let us
think, as we lay stone on stone, that a time
is to come when those stones will be held
sacred because our hands have touched them,
and that men will say as they look upon them,
See this our fathers did for us.

RUSKIN

THE ROMANS had the will to conquer, to colonize, and to build.
During the 500 years of their supremacy, Roman engineers made
such progress that from the second century they were producing
works which, at their best, came near to perfection. There is little
doubt that their earliest bridges were built in timber, but none
has survived, and we know relatively little of their construction.
But the mighty bridges and aqueducts they have left in stone, the
huge amphitheatres capable of seating thousands of persons, and
the undeviating lines of their military roads seem to be the
work of a race of giants. It is small wonder that Marshal Ney,
pointing to some modern reconstruction on the towering Roman
aqueduct of Segovia, said, 'C'est ici que commence le travail des
hommes'.

The Roman empire spread until, under Trajan, its highways
stretched across France, Germany, and Britain, penetrated
westwards into Spain and east beyond the Danube to Asia Minor.
All over England we find traces of them, from Ermine Street and
Watling Street converging on London, where the Romans
built the first timber bridge across the Thames, to Hadrian's Wall
that formed an east-west barrier against the Picts and Scots in the
North. Not only the network of roads remains, but also parts of
the walls the Romans built surrounding cities such as York or
Chichester, walls on which one can still walk to-day; and,
scattered over the countryside, many lesser remains of camps

and earthworks such as the beech-covered crest of the Downs at
Chanctonbury Ring.

> And see you, after rain, the trace
> Of mound and ditch and wall?
> O that was a Legion's camping-place,
> When Cæsar sailed from Gaul.

Much has come down to us of Roman ways. We know of the
cement they made, a little of the tools and plant they used; we
know something of the labour they employed, the various means
of financing their building, and their methods of construction.
But there are some tantalizing gaps. We know the names of some
of their bridge-builders, such as Caius Julius Lacer, the creator of
the majestic Alcantara bridge, and Apollodorus of Damascus who
built the bridge over the Danube; but what manner of men these
were, how far their technical knowledge had developed, and
under what conditions they worked will probably never now be
known.

Perhaps the most important discovery of the Roman builders
was that of a natural cement. This was pozzuolana, a loosely
coherent volcanic sand found at Pozzuoli near Naples, that forms
a hydraulic cement when mixed with ordinary lime. The Romans
mixed their cement in the ratio of two parts by weight of pozzuolana to one of lime. This enabled them to make lime mortar or
concrete. They made considerable use of concrete in foundations,
particularly those built under water. The Romans were also
accomplished brick-makers. Their bricks were shaped like large
tiles, either triangular or a foot or more square, and from an inch
to an inch and a half thick. They were made of clay, earth, and
sand, were allowed to dry out very thoroughly, and proved to
have good lasting qualities through the years.

In their campaigns the Romans used fords or ferries, if they
could be found, as river crossings; elsewhere boat, raft, or timber
trestle bridges were made. Caesar's famous Rhine bridge (55 B.C.)
of which schoolboys read in *De Bello Gallico* was one of these.
Trestles, each consisting of four raking[1] piles of timber 18 inches
thick, were driven into the bed of the river. The pairs of piles
were set 40 feet apart at the base and sloped together at the top,
where they were joined by a 24-inch-wide cross timber. The
trestles were then interconnected by logs laid from one to the
other and floored with long poles and wattlework. More raking

[1] Inclined from the perpendicular.

piles were driven downstream and joined to the bridge to resist the force of the current; others were driven upstream to act as fenders and take the shock of tree trunks or vessels launched by the enemy against the structure. Although the Rhine bridge was probably more than 1,000 feet long, Caesar triumphantly claims that it was completed in ten days.

Bridges of a more permanent character were built with timber superstructure on stone piers, but the most important were made wholly in stone. A famous example of composite construction is that of Trajan's bridge over the Danube, built by Apollodorus of Damascus in A.D. 106 (Fig. 4). At the site, the Danube is nearly three-quarters of a mile wide. The ruins of some of the bridge piers were said to be still visible in the last century below

FIG. 4. Part of Trajan's bridge over the Danube as it is shown in the relief on Trajan's column. Many of the details are out of scale, and in particular the height of the latticed parapet above the roadway is much exaggerated.

the rapids of the Iron Gate. The bridge is illustrated in a relief on Trajan's column, but it is very questionable to what extent the details shown represent what was actually built. There is a description of the bridge in a history of Rome written by Dion Cassius about a hundred years later, which is very much at variance with the structure shown on Trajan's column. According to Dion Cassius, the bridge had twenty piers of hewn stone each 150 feet high, 60 feet wide, and 50 feet thick. The openings between the piers were spanned by timber arches 110 feet long.

At first this sounds rather ambitious, as there is no record of any other timber bridge built by the Romans of such a span. However, it is hard to overlook or explain away the evidence of the remains of the piers. According to some authorities, the first piers were built on a small tongue of land projecting into the river. Then a canal was dug through the spit of land to cause a partial diversion of the water, the soil being deposited in midstream to form an embankment for the reduced width of the river. After that the work became more complicated. Timber cofferdams were driven around the site of each pier and the water drained out of them so that the piers could be built in the dry. It is difficult to reconcile this description with the account given by Alfred Leger, who states that the Romans sank boats filled with quarry stones, so as to form a uniform floor on the river bed, continuous from one bank to the other, upon which the piers were afterwards erected.

The bas-relief on Trajan's column shows the spans each consisting of three concentric timber arches. A flight of steps led to the roadway which was closed at each end by a monumental gateway and drawbridge, and protected by a fortified citadel. The bridge was evidently built by legionaries for the inscriptions of three auxiliary cohorts are found engraved on bricks among the ruins. The following inscription was also found: *Providentia Augusti vere pontificis virtus romana quid non domet sub jugum ecce rapidus et Danubius*.[1] In spite of this confident prophecy, however, the bridge did not last long; the superstructure was destroyed by the Romans themselves, less than thirty years later, to prevent the incursion of the Dacians into the empire.

The remains of some Roman bridges in England also throw light on their methods of composite construction in timber and stone. Excavations in the river Trent near South Collingham in 1885 disclosed the remains of two massive masonry piers some 20 feet apart. The piers were diamond-shaped, 31 feet long and 10 feet wide, and the masonry was bound round with a framework of solid oak timbering. It appeared that the framework must have been made on land and subsequently lowered into position, after which it was filled with rubble masonry bedded in hard-setting mortar. The piers evidently formed part of a bridge of eight spans which had been built diagonally across the river. It is of interest to note that, although the Trent is 240 feet wide at this part, the Romans did not bother to change the direction of the road so as to cross the river by the shortest route. No trace of any arch stones was found in the river bed, so that it is assumed that the roadway was carried on timber beams. So solid were the piers that they had to be blown up with dynamite to clear the bed of the river.

Excavations of the remains of the Roman bridge across the North Tyne at Chesters have disclosed the existence of two bridges

[1] The Roman Augustus, truly a great bridge-builder, wrought this bridge which even the mighty Danube cannot subdue.

on the same site. The stone abutment of the bridge where the line of Hadrian's Wall crossed the river was found to enclose the foundation of the pier of a much smaller bridge which was evidently built before the Great Wall was planned. Its width could have been no more than was necessary for the passage of foot soldiers. Nor has any trace of masonry arches been found. Again, therefore, the inference is that the superstructure must have been of timber, and it has been suggested that the first bridge may have been used to carry the wall over the river on massive lintels of oak.

*　　*　　*

The Romans built on the grand scale. Some of their viaducts were as much as 160 feet high and their arches of 140-foot span— dimensions that are rarely exceeded to-day. All their great stone bridges have similar characteristics. They invariably used the semi-circular arch and never built it with a rise less than a third of the span.

An obvious advantage of the circular arch, especially to the Romans who shaped the voussoirs with the greatest accuracy, is that all the arch stones can be cut identically. Probably for this reason and on account of their success with the circular shape, the Romans never tried any other kind. Inferior craftsmen in the Middle Ages had recourse to pointed arches which required less skill to build, exerted less thrust on the abutments, and were less susceptible to failure through subsidence of the crown. The first pointed arch to appear in the West is in the biggest of the three aqueducts built at Bourgas near Constantinople (A.D. 395).

The piers of the Roman arches were made very thick, the average width being about a third of the span. In a multi-arch bridge, therefore, every pier was strong enough to act as an abutment. Thus the destruction of one or more arches would not bring down the remainder. Like their roads the bridges were narrow and the highways, which usually rose steeply towards the middle of the bridge, were flanked with pavements and raised parapets.

Arches were built with the intrados and extrados[1] parallel, and stones of huge size and weight were used. According to Alfred Leger, the average compression stress in Roman arches was about double that usually adopted to-day, but thanks to the admirable precision of the joints no undue settlement resulted. Stones to be

---

[1] Intrados, the interior or lower line of an arch.
   Extrados, the exterior or upper line of an arch.

used as voussoirs were cut and fitted so perfectly that there was no need for mortar at the connections. Iron or bronze cramps were used between the stones of each ring, but not transversely. Curiously enough, although the builders could mark off and cut the stones with such precision, the spans of what were obviously intended to be equal arches varied considerably. The two spans of the Pons Fabricius (62 B.C.) measured 24.24 and 24.50 metres; the spans of the Pons Augustus measured 8.71, 8.86, 10.56, 8.92, and 8.01 metres. The spandrels of the arches were often pierced with niches or relief arches, to reduce the obstruction offered by the bridge in times of flood. Blunt triangular cutwaters[1] were constructed, usually both up and downstream.

The weakest part of the Roman bridges was their foundations. Like all other engineers, the Romans much preferred to build them in the dry, and they appear to have had little confidence in their foundations built below water. They seem to have appreciated the necessity of spreading the base over a wide area, particularly on soft ground; but they often failed to go deep enough to obtain a good foundation; nor did they take adequate precautions to prevent the piers from being undermined by scour. It is strange that although they used rock filling to protect moles and jetties against waves, they rarely if ever used stone pitching around the piers of their bridges to protect them from undermining. It was by failure of the foundations through settlement or scour that most of their bridges ultimately fell. Some of them were rebuilt three or four times by the Romans themselves. Those that have come down to us owe their survival largely to the strength and durability of the ground on which they were built.

For foundations in shallow water in reasonably good ground the Romans built cofferdams of timber piles to surround the site, and then poured in concrete through the water. If the ground was poor they built a cofferdam with a double row of sheathing and filled in the space between the timbers with rammed clay in bags. Having thus made it more or less watertight, they emptied the cofferdam by means of water wheels or scoops. Then they dug out the worst of the ground, but they could go to no great depth. If the ground was still poor they might even drive bearing piles of alder, olive, or oak. Thereafter they could build the piers in the dry on top of the piles.

Marcus Vitruvius Pollio, writing of foundations, refers to the necessity for using bearing piles, and says moreover that the wood must be previously charred to prevent corrosion and the piles

---

[1] Sharp or rounded projections on the ends of bridge piers.

must be driven by a machine. A bad fault, however, appears to have been that the Romans usually stopped driving at the first refusal, even if this occurred when the pile was only 10 feet into the ground, instead of driving not less than 15 or 20 feet deep.

In deep water they had recourse to lowering box-like timber frameworks subsequently to be filled with rock, onto the bed of the river. Alternatively, concrete blocks might be used as was done, according to Vitruvius, in the foundations of the jetties in the Larbour at Samos. Aristotle records that the ancients used to employ divers armed with tubes communicating with the air, or diving bells lowered vertically, to control the placing of rock or stone below water. In the Aelius bridge, which spanned the Tiber where it was narrow and deep, the Romans are said to have sunk the foundations to a depth of 16 feet below river bed. With their comparatively primitive plant and tools, this must have been work of the utmost difficulty. But their efforts were rewarded, and although the bridge was built more than 1,800 years ago, the original piers are still standing; the superstructure, however, has been rebuilt and the bridge now goes by the name of Sant' Angelo.

* * *

Information as to the tools the Roman craftsmen used can be found in many sources; in the writings of Vitruvius and Frontin, in bas-reliefs on tombs, on Trajan's column and the Antonine column, on coins, and on Roman and Etruscan pottery. Their surveying instruments included 5-foot rules, squares, plumb-bob, plumb-level and dividers. Their masons used the saw, awl, chisel, mason's axe, bevel, trowel, and wedges. Heavy loads were transported on two- or four-wheeled carts drawn by many horses, or were hauled on rollers on the ground. For lifting they employed cranes, or used systems of pulley blocks, hung from sheer legs or poles, which were worked by means of a winch or capstan. One type of crane is illustrated in a Roman bas-relief showing the building of a temple. This crane had two pulleys, the upper one fixed, and the lower movable one connected to the load. The hoist rope was wound round a winch which was turned by means of a hollow horizontal cylinder, something like a tread-mill. Men entered the cylinder and turned it by trying to climb the rungs on the sides. Heavy stones were lifted by means of slings or gripped by pincers; alternatively, a kind of lewis[1] might be used.

[1] A lifting device which is inserted and wedged into a dovetailed cavity cut in the top of a block of masonry.

For draining foundations, cofferdams, or pits they used the screw pump and water wheels, either singly or in stages one above the other if they had to drain from some depth.

In most places stone was plentiful and the Romans did not stint themselves; but in Rome and the provinces timber was scarce and had to be used economically. Scaffolding was usually made of short pieces of softwood supported on putlogs[1]. Scaffold poles were propped on corbelled stones. These projecting stones and the openings for the putlogs can still be seen in their bridges to-day. The methods employed in building arches were much the same as those we use. Timber centering was built, on which the arch stones were laid; to save timber the arches were sometimes constructed in parallel sections so that the same centering could be used in each. Alternatively, two or more ribs might be built with a space between, which was spanned by deck slabs or masonry.

As in our own day, the grants set aside by the Treasury for public works were relatively meagre, and bridges had generally to be financed by local resources or private enterprise. Townships spent enthusiastically on public works, and ordinary citizens, in order to court favour, subscribed liberally. The Alcantara bridge carries an inscription recording the names of all the towns that contributed to its cost. Forced labour, consisting of slaves, prisoners, or convicts, was generally used. The labour of the legions was employed only on works undertaken at the expense of the Treasury. The emperors, however, frequently sent architects, engineers, and skilled workmen to give supervision and guidance. These experts were formed by the State into semi-military guilds and in return for exemption from certain taxes they gave the State their service, and could not even refuse to follow the legions in their farthest expeditions. This gathering together of experts and exchange of knowledge and ideas was of the greatest benefit. In the course of their travels the members of the guild spread new methods and ideas abroad; this accounts for the family likeness, as it were, in all the widespread monuments of the Roman empire. The guilds formed the basis of colleges in which professional standards were laid down, technical methods recommended, and faulty practices prohibited. They may be considered the Roman equivalent of our British Standards Institution and Institution of Civil Engineers. Through them were slowly formulated the laws of the art of building, as subsequently drawn up by Vitruvius.

*   *   *

[1] Cross-piece in scaffolding, the inner end resting in a hole left in the wall.

The first bridge to be built in Rome was the famous Pons Sublicius that Horatius, Lartius, and Herminius defended so heroically in the face of the Etruscan host under Lars Porsena.

> Stout Lartius hurled down Aunus
> Into the stream beneath;
> Herminius struck at Seius,
> And clove him to the teeth:
> At Picus brave Horatius
> Darted one fiery thrust;
> And the proud Umbrian's gilded arms
> Clashed in the bloody dust.

The bridge derived its name from the 'sublicae' or wooden beams of which it was constructed, and was for many years the only bridge across the Tiber. Tradition says that it was originally built by Ancus Marcius, and made wholly in timber because the temporary character of a wooden bridge would offer less offence to Father Tiber than a permanent bridge in stone. Even so, victims had to be offered to appease the river gods; this was done originally by means of human sacrifice and later by casting into the river every year thirty dummies made of rushes which were known as 'argei'. When the bridge was reconstructed the piers were built of stone, but timber had to be used for the superstructure. Not a scrap of iron was permitted in the construction. According to Lanciani the reason for this was that the Romans still lived morally in the Bronze Age and had feelings of repulsion for the new metal. These feelings have been paralleled in comparatively recent times, as witness William Morris's censure of iron in the construction of the Forth Bridge (*see* p. 115). They were so strong in Roman days that even the use of iron tools was forbidden in the repair of sacred temples. The Pons Sublicius was finally carried away by a flood in A.D. 69 and now even the exact site is unknown to us.

The oldest bridge in Rome which is still standing and practically intact was built by Lucius Fabricius, Commissioner of Roads in 62 B.C. (Fig. 5). It is known as Quattro Capi, after the four-headed figure of Jason which once supported the panels of the parapet. It has two main arches, and joins the island of Aesculapius to the left bank of the river. The island housed the Temple of Aesculapius, to which the Romans resorted for the cure of all kinds of ailments. In those days the island was fashioned like a huge ship with prow, stem, and sides formed of travertine,[1] and a central obelisk erected to represent a mast. On the other side of the island was the Pons Cestius built in 60-36 B.C. by Lucius Cestius, one-time governor of Rome. These two bridges, flanking the island ship, must have made a striking group. A panel (of 21 B.C.) on the Pons Frabricius certifies that the work has been truly and satis-factorily done. This refers to a wise if somewhat drastic principle of Roman administration, that the builders of bridges were held

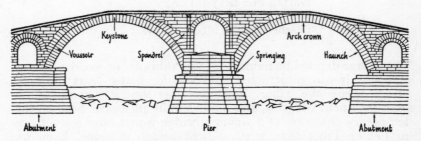

FIG. 5. The Pons Fabricius before the building of the present Tiber embankments, which now hide the small arches in the abutments. The drawing shows ap-proximately the original state of the bridge, and is based on an engraving in Piranesi's *Le Antichita Romane*, 1756.

responsible for their stability for forty years, after which time they were repaid the deposit which had been required of them.

*   *   *

In A.D. 134 the emperor Hadrian completed the famous Aelius bridge which has now become the bridge of Sant' Angelo. There were originally seven arches over the river, the longest having a span of nearly 60 feet, and the roadway was some 34 feet wide. The foundations, which have lasted to this day, appear to be very extensive. Engravings by Piranesi show the piers founded on a platform of masonry built across the bed of the river from bank to bank, the river being partially diverted while the work was done. A similar kind of construction was found recently to have been used on the foundations of the Pons Cestius. According to a drawing published by Alfred Leger, however, each pier of the Aelius bridge was built on a separate foundation.

The construction of the bridge was recorded on two inscriptions

[1] A hard grey limestone frequently used in Rome.

which were lost in a great catastrophe in 1450. On 19 December of that year, when large crowds were returning from St. Peter's, a mule belonging to one of the Cardinals became restive and caused a panic. Under the pressure of the stampeding crowds, the parapet gave way, 172 pilgrims fell into the river and many were drowned. The arch gateways built originally at each end lasted until the fifteenth century, when the bridge was rebuilt on the existing piers by Popes Nicholas V and Clement IX. In the seventeenth century it was widened and ornamented with the statues of angels and fine balustrade by Bernini which are still to be seen to-day.

* * *

Some of the mightiest and most impressive Roman bridges, which fall broadly into two groups, are to be found in Spain. On the one hand there is the long low bridge of many nearly equal arches across a broad river valley. Of this kind are the bridges of Salamanca, Cordova, and Merida. As a contrast there is the majestic lofty bridge of few and unequal arches thrown across a wide rocky gorge.

Such is the Alcantara bridge over the Tagus (Pl. 1). Set in rugged mountainous country, the great stone arches span the gorge of the river at an unbelievable height. The roadway over the top of the bridge is 170 feet above the bed of the river; higher than the railway which runs across the Firth of Forth. Founded in solid rock, the mighty granite piers, 30 feet square[1], rise tall and majestic to the springing of the two centre arches each of 98-foot span. So they have stood for nearly 2,000 years, month in, month out, whether the diminished river flowed beneath in the summer drought, or flood waters swirled past in an irresistible torrent. In the words of E.T.A. Wigram:

'All is vast and huge and desolate; the sun itself hardly shows in such a picture; yet in the midst one object catches the eye which seems to challenge comparison even with nature itself—the work of Titans rather than men—The Bridge—Al Kántarah.[2] Spain is the land of bridges. In all Europe they have few rivals, but here they own a King. Since the day when Caius Julius Lacer finished his great work for the Emperor Trajan, and was laid to rest beside it, no other bridge has ever challenged comparison with this—a work to vie with the Pyramids of Egypt or the Flavian Amphi-

---

[1] Excluding the triangular cutwaters on the upstream face.
[2] 'Al Kántarah' is Moorish for 'the bridge'.

theatre at Rome. . . . Our eyes may still behold a memorial which nature has assailed in vain— "Pontem Perpetui Mansuram in Saecula Mundi"[1]—the monument of Caius Julius Lacer, more enduring even than Wren's.'

The voussoirs consist of stones of great size, shaped and dressed with such precision that no mortar is needed or used. There is little decoration; the archivolts[2] project without any imposts[3] at the springings; square buttresses jut out sharply and extend from the top of the pier to the coping, above which runs a solid parapet. Above one of the middle piers rises a typical feature of Roman bridges, a fortified gateway; at each end of the bridge were triumphal arches which have now been destroyed.

No record of how the bridge was built has come down to us, but with only primitive Roman plant and tackle it must have been a redoubtable task. We do not know how the centering was arranged or supported; but the widest spans would have been over water all the year round. Moreover, each arch must have been quickly completed, because no supports or scaffolding would have been able to withstand the frequent floods. For lifting the arch stones, which weighed up to 8 tons and had to be raised more than 150 feet, some kind of crane, possibly of the type described above, must have been used. Until 1214 the bridge stood intact, then the Moors in wartime breached one of the small arches. In 1812 the French, in the face of the Duke of Wellington's army, destroyed one of the 98-foot spans. The British under Colonel Sturgeon built a suspension bridge of ropes across the gap, which proved strong enough for the passage of the Duke's siege artillery. The arch has since been repaired in the native granite, but in spite of no mortar having been used in the original building, the restorers found it necessary to point the joints.

*   *   *

Another of the most famous Roman monuments is the mighty three-tiered aqueduct, known as the Pont du Gard, near Nîmes (Pl. 2). The exact date of construction is unknown, nor do we even know the name of the builder. Stretching across the valley of the river Gard, an affluent of the Rhône, the lowest tier consists

---

[1] I have left a bridge that shall remain for eternity.

[2] Archivolt, the band or moulding which runs round the lower part of the arch stones.

[3] Impost, a column in a pier or abutment beneath the springing of an arch.

of six arches from 50 to 80 feet in span. Above them rises the second row of arches, eleven in number on account of the increased width of the valley. The third and highest tier, which carried the water channel, consists of thirty-five smaller arches of about 16-foot diameter. The design is unusually bold in that the ratio of thickness of piers to span of arch is only one fifth, instead of the usual Roman ratio of one third.

The overall length of the aqueduct is about 860 feet and the height of the water channel is more than 160 feet above the river. The channel itself is about 4 feet wide and 6 feet high; it is now, of course, dry, and a thick chalky deposit can be seen in layers on the sides. The stones forming the pipe were carefully cemented, and the channel covered on top with stone slabs. All the other stones in the aqueduct were cut exactly to shape and laid dry. Not even metal clamps were used to hold them together. All the arches are semi-circular, and the vaults of the lowest tier are built up of four independent sections side by side. Many of the ashlar stones, brought from a quarry on the left bank of the river, are more than 4 feet cube and weigh 6 tons. Just above the springing of each arch is a ledge formed by projecting voussoirs which served to support the centering when the arches were built.

Like most contemporary works, it has suffered terrible depredations, the most serious occurring in the seventeenth century when the south of France was ravaged by religious wars. It was then determined, although the bridge carried no roadway, to use it for the transport of artillery. To make a road, the stonework at the side of the piers of the second tier was cut away. In a short time this would have brought the whole structure down in ruins, had not the governor of Languedoc seen the danger and repaired the damage. Even so the aqueduct now appears to lean slightly upstream due to settlement that took place at that time. In 1747 a roadway was built close to the downstream face, carried on new arches of the same size as the existing ones. The value of the Pont du Gard as a monument led to its complete restoration in 1855, since when no pains have been spared to keep it in good preservation. Most people would agree that in the fine proportions of its mellow arches, and the grandeur of its conception and setting, the Pont du Gard eclipses anything of a similar nature that has been built since.

Chapter 3

PERSIA, CHINA, AND JAPAN

The City [Sin-din-fu, now called Ching-to-fu]
is watered by many considerable streams, which,
descending from the distant mountains, surround
and pass through it in a variety of directions.
Some of these rivers are half a mile in width,
others are two hundred paces, and very deep,
over which are built several large and handsome
stone bridges, eight paces in breadth, their
length being greater or less according to the
size of the stream.   From one extremity to the
other there is a row of marble pillars on each
side, which support the roof; for here the
bridges have very handsome roofs, constructed
of wood, ornamented with paintings of a red
colour, and covered with tiles. Throughout
the whole length also there are neat apartments
and shops, where all sorts of trades are carried
on.

MARCO POLO (1254-1324)

IN CHINA and to a considerable extent in Persia bridges developed
independently of the western world. An account of them therefore
cuts across the chronology of our subject, but their problems are so
peculiarly their own and their bridges so distinctive that it seems
best to deal with them in one chapter. Owing to her clash with
Rome, Persian bridges, as we shall see, were much affected by
Roman practice. China, however, suffered no conquest, and had
little traffic with the West until a much later age. Her methods of
building continued undisturbed.

In Persia wide deserts and jagged rocky uplands almost barren
of wood or vegetation compelled engineers to find ways of
building without or with very little timber. They were sometimes

forced to use only brick centering[1] for their stone arches or, if it could be found, very light timberwork, covered with concentric rings of brickwork. No doubt this was one of the reasons that made their engineers prefer the pointed arch, because its shape imposed less load on the centering and a smaller thrust at the end than a circular arch. After the Roman conquest the semi-circular arch appeared in the East, and there is a fine example in the doorway of the fifth-century Persian citadel of Shouster. The use of brick centering only would probably have been impracticable but for the discovery of gypsum mortar. This was made from Paget stone found on the Mesopotamian plateau, and binds the bricks together

FIG. 6. The Shouster bridge over the Karun river. Later Persian arches are built on Roman piers, which follow the curving line of the rock outcrops across the river.

mechanically rather than by the formation of a chemical compound. Over the Iran of the Taq-i-Kisra in Ctesiphon (A.D. 531-79) there is a huge parabolic arch of 84-foot span. The vault of this arch is roofed with vertical courses, pointed in gypsum mortar, and is the largest example of this type of construction.

Some of the Persian bridges such as Shouster and Ab-i-Diz have Roman as well as Persian characteristics. The explanation of this is that Shapur I, after his victory over the Romans under Valerian in A.D. 260, employed Roman prisoners on the works. The Shouster bridge over the Karun river has a length of 1,693 feet and is carried on forty-one piers; these are spaced closely together as the bridge was also intended to act as a dam (Fig. 6). In fact

[1] In brick centering the first ring of brickwork is supported by jointing it on to a temporary cross wall built at one side of the arch. Sometimes the rings of brickwork are built sloping towards the wall to give them additional stability.

the width of the piers is substantially greater than that of the openings between them. The core of the bridge piers is of rubble faced with masonry in the Roman manner. Another typically Roman feature is the formation of relief openings in the spandrels of the bridge to assist in times of flood.

The use of a bridge to serve also as a dam is not uncommon in Persia, where the scarcity of water necessitates impounding it in reservoirs for irrigation of the land. The Shouster bridge exhibits another characteristic peculiar to Persian bridges. As engineers had neither the material nor the knowledge to build cofferdams, they had to locate the bridge piers wherever there happened to be existing islands in the river bed. For this reason the bridge winds its way across the river, following the line of the stone out-crops, and not even the spans of the arches could be kept uniform. It was not easy to find suitable sites of this nature and therefore, in direct opposition to the Roman practice, roads in Persia used to be diverted to a site convenient for the bridge.

Both Roman and Persian methods are blended in the Shahristan bridge below Isfahan. Here the piers are provided with triangular cutwaters, the arches are pointed, and the ratio of arch span to width of pier is higher than in the bridges at Shouster or Dizful. The area of the relief openings is also greater; in fact the bridge is of a higher standard of design.

One of the most famous Persian bridges is that at Dizful, built according to tradition by a Sassanide Prince, Adéchir I, in the fourth century. It has an overall length of 1,250 feet, and is the first of the Persian bridges in which Roman methods were used. The oldest arches are elliptical; later ones are of the ogival shape which is said to go back to the times of Haroun-al-Raschid. The bridge is very heavy, with piers 30 feet thick and openings between them of only 23 feet. It shows traces of many restorations; most of the arches have been rebuilt in brick, but thanks to the strong subsoil of 'pudding-stone',[1] all but three of the original piers are standing. This bridge was one of three built on a strategic road crossing the Kerkha, Abdizful, and Karun rivers. The bridge at Kerkha has long been down in ruins, but the piers of the other two have withstood the floods for fifteen centuries.

Amongst later works is the Red bridge, on the road from Tiflis to Tauris, consisting of four pointed arches, the biggest of which has a span of nearly 100 feet. This was built in the middle of the eleventh century, and is not unlike some of the medieval bridges in France. There is also the fine-looking bridge of the Young Maiden

[1] A conglomerate rock made up of rounded pebbles.

built four centuries later over the river Kisilon-Son. The river, which is deep and unfordable for five months of the year, is spanned by three arches. The art of building foundations below water must have spread to Persia before this date. The arches have a rise of 78 feet; they are built of small bricks and carry an inscription in praise of Allah.

In Persia, as in Europe, toll and custom houses were built on bridges; fortified guard rooms and tall watch towers were also established, especially if the river formed a boundary between rival states. It is not difficult to picture the long caravans toiling

FIG. 7. The Pul-i-Khaju at Isfahan.

over the desert, the camel bells tinkling as the travellers made their parched and dusty way through the guarded gateways of the bridge, seeking rest and refreshment in the cool shaded pavilions and caravanserai to be found upon it. For to the Persians, bridges were much more than simply a means of crossing a river. By the seventeenth century some of them, such as the Allahverdi-Khan and Pul-i-Khaju, were designed as delightful retreats from the heat and dust of the desert (Fig. 7). High walls bounded the roadway and separated it from arcaded footways that ran either side for the length of the bridge. Here pedestrians could enjoy cool breezes and pleasant views of the river. Moreover, rooms were provided for shelter and entertainment, whose walls were ornamented with paintings designed to charm the weary traveller.

The culmination of this trend is found in the famous Pul-i-Khaju at Isfahan, without doubt one of the great bridges of the world, in which Shah Abbas II (1642-67) contrived with imagination and taste to exploit the possibilities of the site to the utmost. The superstructure is built on a dam which impounds the river to a height of six feet. From this reservoir irrigation channels lead the water to the fertile lands on either side. The dam is of stone, pierced by narrow openings, the flow through which is regulated by sluices. The bridge is 85 feet wide and consists of some twenty-four brick arches with an overall length of 462 feet. It is two-storied, and the arrangement of the roads and footways is somewhat similar to those on the Allahverdi-Khan. Above low water level, there is a wide roadway sufficient for five lanes of traffic; in addition there is an enclosed roadway above and three or four passages for pedestrians. To quote Arthur Upham Pope:

'The lower half of the bridge really forms a long series of vaulted bays. Down the long centre axis there opens a magnificent vista of successive piers, arches, and vaults like a vastly prolonged aisle of some huge crypt. Each vault rests upon four square stone piers which in turn stand on a wide masonry platform where in perpetual shade and cooling breezes one may enjoy concentrated vistas downstream of the mountains and the sunrise, and upstream to more mountains and sunsets more gorgeous. From the steps on the lower side of the bridge the people wash their linen or play in the cool water, and interior stairways lead thence up to the second storey of the bridge. Here there is a long arcade of niches, as in the bridge of Allahverdi-Khan, though more spacious, each a little outdoor room capable of holding half a dozen persons. Poets in contemplation, mullahs and philosophers in argument, families in reunion, gossiping women and friends at various amusements, all may enjoy the beauties of the scene in isolation and contentment.'

Such is the Pul-i-Khaju, its majesty enhanced by the loftiness of the upper pointed arches and the six tall hexagonal pavilions, two in the centre and one at each corner, which project from the face of the bridge and tower above it. Together with Old London bridge in its prime and the Ponte Vecchio in Florence, it constitutes one of the great bridges that were closely linked by the buildings on them to the multitudinous life of their times.

*   *   *

In the primitive villages of China,[1] all three types of bridge, beams, arches, and suspension spans, are to be found. The early simple spans consisted of timber beams borne on piles of soft fir wood, driven 5 or 6 feet into the river bed, and paved with small branches placed crosswise and covered with clay. Probably several thousand years ago these bridges began to be superseded by stone structures, because the timber decayed too quickly in the warm damp climate. The foundations of the stone bridges were built in shallow cofferdams. The sides of these were composed of double walls of bamboo mats, lashed to poles, the space between the walls being filled with clay. The water was pumped out of the cofferdam by means of tread pumps, and large flat stones were laid to make the foundation in the bed of the creek. A narrow wall parallel to the stream was then built to a height above water level by morticing vertical stones into the foundations. These pier shafts were then capped with another horizontal stone, on which the decking slabs of the bridge were laid. Bridges of this kind varied in width from little more than a foot to upwards of 6 feet.

The most extraordinary of these structures is the Poh Lam bridge built in medieval times over the Dragon river in Fukien. This bridge, which has an overall length of 1,100 feet, might have been modelled on the wooden cantilever bridges of Kashmir. The piers are corbelled out at the top by horizontal stones 20 feet long; the longest spans, which measure 70 feet, are composed of three stones of enormous length and weight. These huge blocks of granite are 5 feet wide, 6 feet deep, and weigh as much as 200 tons each. The secret of how they were quarried, transported, and erected is as great a mystery as the building of Stonehenge.

The Poh Lam bridge is still standing, but where spans have fallen, they have been reconstructed as two shorter spans by building an intermediate pier. According to Fugl-Meyer spans of 70 feet are the maximum that can be built with the kind of granite used.

Such bridges are confined to Fukien; they were all built within a short period and are found nowhere else in the world. It seems very probable, therefore, that they are all the work of the same genius, whose secret died with him, and whose name we shall never know.

*   *   *

[1] For this section on Chinese bridges I am indebted to H. Fugl-Meyer for the excellent account given in his book *Chinese Bridges*, 1937

When rivers were too wide to be bridged by beams, wooden cantilever bridges were built. The two cantilever arms consisted of numbers of tree trunks, projecting out nearly horizontally from abutments on the banks. The land ends of the timbers were weighted down with rocks and the two adjacent ends over the river were joined by wooden beams. Bridges of this kind, which are still being built to-day, may have spans up to 150 feet.

*   *   *

Primitive suspension bridges are built in Western China of ropes 2 inches thick made of plaited bamboo strands. The simplest and most unpleasant kind of bridge consisted of only two ropes hung across the river, one five feet or so above the other. The intrepid traveller had to walk on the lower rope and hold the upper one. What happened when the top rope swung one way and the lower one the other may be left to our imagination! Sometimes a double rope was provided to walk on and the cables were tied together vertically at intervals. The form of these Chinese bridges is quite different from the suspension bridges of three ropes found in the Himalayas; the two types meet in Tibet. In more important bridges the deck may be carried on a number of bamboo cables hanging at the same level and interconnected. Cable handrails are provided on either side. In the strongly built stone bridge houses at each end of the span are primitive capstans, consisting of vertical wooden columns, to which individual cables are attached. By turning the columns, the cables can be loosened or tautened, like huge violin strings. As the life of the cables is very short the capstans are in regular use. The most impressive bridge of this kind is that at Kwan Hsien, which has an overall length of 700 feet, the longest span being 200 feet. The bridge has four intermediate piers, and the cables have to be replaced annually.

It was no doubt the short life of bamboo cables which led to their replacement in some instances by iron chains, which appear to have been introduced in bridges in the Indus Valley some 2,000 years ago. They are arranged in the same way as the bamboo cables but are rigidly anchored at the ends without any kind of capstan adjustment. In Szechuan there is a unique suspension bridge supported by iron eyebars $2\frac{1}{4}$ inches in diameter. The overall length of the bridge is 300 feet and it is divided into four spans by wide stone piers. These piers are convex on top; the eyebars pass over them in a reverse curve. The roadway is built on the cables, and undulates across the river, dipping down between the piers and rising over the top of them.

*   *   *

It is perhaps the Chinese arch bridges which present the most extraordinary features (Fig. 8). Owing to the impossibility of building rigid foundations in the spongy plastic silt of the Yangtse delta, the Chinese developed their arches on the principle of resisting by yielding. The stone vaults of the arches were built of thin curved stone slabs joined end to end, covered with more

FIG. 8. A fine example of a Chinese arch bridge at Quinsan in Kiangsu province. Note the flexible stone arches, which can deform considerably before failing, and the ends of the vertical cross walls between them.

stones placed crosswise, and loose rubble filling. The filling was contained by means of vertical side walls resting on the arch and bonded into the rubble. These bridges might thus be described as consisting of stone chains employed in compression.

This form of construction gave the arches amazing flexibility and they could easily adapt themselves to the rise and fall of the silt foundations and the weight of traffic. The bridges were high and narrow; they had stone steps at the approaches and, like the bridges described by Marco Polo, were usually covered. The arches were originally built circular, but seldom remained true to shape for long. When they failed it was with little warning and they collapsed like a pack of cards. No mortar was used and the joints between stones were made by morticing them or sometimes by means of dovetailed iron keys. The minimum quantity of stone was used and the shells of the arches were daringly thin. The thickness of the crown varied from one-thirtieth to one-sixtieth of the span which compares well with modern reinforced concrete practice.

The hidden strength of these bridges no doubt lies in the internal vertical walls that were built across the full width of the arch and projected through and beyond the side walls. These cross walls were located immediately behind each abutment and over the piers. Loads that tended to deform the arch were transmitted through the filling and so resisted by these walls. The foundations were built in cofferdams and the arch stones laid on temporary planking supported by bamboo staging.

*   *   *

Japan is the home of the small picturesque bridge of timber arches, frequently built without the use of a single metal nail or bolt. Christian Barman[1] cites Japanese bridges as examples of 'exquisitely perfected temporary construction'. Bridges and temples were often rebuilt annually. The famous Kintai-kyo bridge at Iwakuni used to have its five arches rebuilt in succession, so that the whole bridge was renewed every twenty-five years. According to Japanese belief structures must never be allowed to fall into decay as that would enfeeble the spirit of continuity on which the survival of mankind depends.

[1] Frank Brangwyn and Christian Barman, *The Bridge*, 1926.

Chapter 4

THE MIDDLE AGES

The bridge is a veritable esquire, bearing arms
of its own (a ship and bridge proper on a plain
field), and owning lands and tenements in many
parishes, with which the said miraculous bridge
has, from time to time, founded charities, built
schools, waged suits at law, and finally given
yearly dinners, and kept for that purpose
(luxurious and liquorish bridge that it was)
the best stocked cellar of wines in all Devon.

CHARLES KINGSLEY on Bideford Bridge in *Westward Ho!*

TRAVELLERS in the Middle Ages had to be hardy. Medieval
carriages were heavy lumbering vehicles, built to stand up to
endless bumps and jolts. They were so comfortless that people of
worth, if they could, rode on horseback, and in the winter were
cloaked to the ears. They had to be alert against attack by
bandits, especially at fords or the approaches to bridges. And in
spite of all their determination they might well be delayed for
days by bad weather which made the roads impassable. In France
no straight roads were laid down after the Romans left until the
formation many centuries later of the Corps des Ingénieurs des
Ponts et Chaussées. There was little internal trade; and goods
were generally carried by pack mule. Bridges were a rare luxury,
not taken for granted as they are to-day. Before the reign of
Louis XIV there were great areas of countryside without any
bridges at all; if rivers were too deep to be forded travellers had to
cross by boat.

After the fall of the Roman empire, apart from a few enlightened
periods, such as during the rule of Charlemagne, bridge-building
languished for nearly eight centuries. In the reigning state of
anarchy and chaos few repairs were made. Even if bridges
escaped destruction by the barons in their feudal wars, they

were allowed to fall into ruin and decay. During the Middle Ages the ogival, or pointed, arch made its appearance in Europe. Due to Persian, Moslem, and Byzantine influence, it spread west to the Atlantic coast and north along the river valleys of the Rhône and Loire to Normandy and Britain. When bridge-building recommenced, the pointed arch was more widely used in France, but the semi-circular shape remained predominant in Italy. In Great Britain both types were adopted, as witness the pointed arches of Old London bridge and the circular arches at Stirling. The masons seem to have lost the art of shaping the stones with the perfection attained by the Romans. Mortar was invariably used in the joints. The pointed arch may have been preferred partly on this account, as its shape demands less precision than the circular form. The stones are to a greater extent supported one on the other and there is less thrust on the abutments.

So far as we can judge, medieval tools and plant showed little advance on those of Roman times. Some of the great wheels belonging to treadmills or hand-operated types of cranes and hoists have been preserved to our day. Hand barrows somewhat similar to stretchers were used, until superseded by wheelbarrows during the Gothic period. Scaffolding was generally made of hurdles instead of sawn planks, which were much too expensive, and leather thongs were employed as lashings. In the thirteenth and fourteenth centuries detailed drawings first came into general use.

In the Middle Ages bridges were not built solely to carry traffic as they are to-day; many other uses were required of them. They were frequently fortified, or even designed as war bridges, to take a dominant part in the defence of a city. Houses, shops, and chapels were built on them; sometimes they became the centres of fairs such as the famous weekly cloth market held on an old bridge in Leeds. They were chosen as the site of tournaments, sports and feats of arms, such as 'water quintain' at Old London bridge and the famous mock battle that was held for three centuries on the bridge at Pisa. In these days some of the earliest timber covered bridges, such as the two over the river Reuss at Lucerne, were constructed. One of these, the Spreuerbrücke, was subsequently decorated with painted panels in the roof representing the 'Danse Macabre'.

Under the feudal system, bridge building and repair flourished in England but deteriorated in France. In England, after the Norman conquest, land was granted to the barons, not in large compact areas, but in the form of a number of widely scattered estates to each. The English kings were in the habit of making frequent journeys about the country. We hear that Edward I changed his dwelling-place no less than seventy-five times in one year. It was thus to the advantage of the highest in the land that bridges should be built and kept in good repair and they saw that the work was done.

In France, however, the barons owned vast single estates, and their interest lay rather in impeding than in improving communications between their lands and those of a rival lord. For this reason they usually opposed the building of a bridge or, if it was built, tried to defend their territory by means of forts at the bridge-head. In many provinces of France the lord had the right to destroy a bridge in time of war, even though he had not contributed towards the cost of building it. Furthermore, his consent had to be obtained before the bridge could be rebuilt. In these circumstances many bridges were partially destroyed to close them to an enemy; subsequently, even if they were repaired at all, the work was scamped and the bridge soon fell.

For the upkeep of most medieval bridges tolls were levied not only on travellers and vehicles using the bridge but also on river traffic passing beneath it. On the Pont St. Esprit for example, a duty known as the 'Petit-Blanc' was levied on salt that was brought up the Rhône. The money was intended to be used for the upkeep of the bridge and the river walls. In the year 1790 as much as 28,000 francs was collected by this means, and then the tax was repealed. In France the feudal lords continued to levy the tax on river traffic even after a bridge had been destroyed. Thus the unfortunate boatmen had to pay for the privilege of navigating past the ruins of piers and arches which might wreck their vessels. In return for the tolls they levied, the barons were expected to ensure the safety of travellers and protect them from bandits and thieves, but it is doubtful how far this obligation was honoured. In later years the right to levy tolls of any kind was vested only in the king.

In England the maintenance of roads and bridges, which was included in the 'trinoda necessitas' (triple obligation), was considered as pious and holy work, on a par with the building of churches. In addition to the income obtained from tolls, offerings were sometimes collected at a chapel on the bridge and the church obtained money for its upkeep from the sale of indulgences. In many cases the lord who founded a bridge gave it a rich endowment. In this way some bridges, such as those at London, Rochester, and Bedford, became not only owners of property or real estate but were also in receipt of income from religious and civil sources. One of the richest bridges in England was that at Bideford which was so liberally endowed that the feoffees, in whose care it was, had not only plenty of money to keep the bridge in good repair but a sufficient surplus to spend on education and charity— for which purpose they appear to have kept 'the best stocked cellar of wines in all Devon'!

We now encounter the phenomenon of the Frères Pontifes, frequently known as the Bridge Brothers or Pontist Friars. The earliest account of the brethren is given by Hubert Gautier in his *Traité des Ponts*, 1714, and reference is made to them by many later writers. According to these accounts the fraternity consisted of groups of public-spirited citizens who banded themselves together, pledged not only to look after the welfare of travellers and the provision of ferries and hostels, but also to build and maintain bridges. Their communities are said to have sprung up by the twelfth century in most countries of Europe but above all in France; although their work might have the sanction of papal bulls, they belonged to none of the four great fraternities of monks; they were organized in independent groups, whose only common bond was charity. The members wore a distinctive costume, white with a red badge on the chest, representing two bridge arches with a cross above them.

According to the legend, if we may so call it, the Frères Pontifes built some of the finest medieval bridges, including the famous Pont d'Avignon and Pont St Esprit. But in looking back to contemporary records a doubt arises. For although St Bénézet, the famous builder of the Pont d'Avignon, is claimed as a leader of the Frères Pontifes, there is in the *Charte Avignonnaise des Actes De St Bénézet*, circa 1230-60, no mention of the existence of any Bridge Brotherhood. Furthermore, Ephraim Emerton, who investigated the question fully some years ago, was forced to the conclusion that 'the more one enquires into the whole subject of the pontifical brethren, the more one is inclined to doubt whether any such order ever existed. The tradition on the subject dies hard though, its tenacity of life owing much probably to the popular appeal of the legend of the saintly Bénézet, who became a patron saint of bridge builders.'

*   *   *

The famous Pont d'Avignon, one of the first bridges to be built in France after the fall of the Roman empire, was begun in 1177 under the direction of St Bénézet. The legend tells that Bénézet came as a stranger to Avignon, inspired by a divine mission to build a bridge there across the Rhône. The river was wide and deep and the town magistrates mocked at his idea. But Bénézet's faith in his mission so inspired the citizens of Avignon and the neighbouring provinces that they hurried to give him all the help he needed. Money was subscribed, materials brought up the river, and all necessary rights and privileges granted. Soon the bridge began to take shape. It stretched across the Rhône valley in a series of lofty arches. Each arch had a span of 100 feet and, resting

FIG. 9. The Pont St Bénézet at Avignon, showing the fine elliptical arches, each built of four parallel rings, and on one of the piers the chapel in which Bénézet was buried. At the foot of this pier can be seen some of the stones from which one of the original arches possibly sprang.

on piers some 25 feet thick, they gave the bridge an overall length of nearly 3,000 feet. The form of the four arches that are standing to-day is entirely novel and it has generally been assumed that they are part of Bénézet's original work (Fig. 9). Recent investigations on the site by Rowland J. Mainstone, however, throw doubt on this point, and it may be that the original arches were built on a slightly different alignment and that those we see were reconstructed, possibly in the fourteenth century. They are elliptical but with major axis vertical, somewhat like an ogival arch but rounded instead of pointed at the crown. The grace and dignity of these slender arches, whether conceived by Bénézet or some unknown genius at a later date, stand out as the work of a master designer.

The site selected was where the Rhône divides into two arms

around the island of Barthelasse. The line of the bridge is not straight but makes an elbow pointing upstream against the current. The change of direction, however, does not occur at the island, but in the middle of the wider channel. A similar alignment is found in the Pont St Esprit. Viollet-le-Duc was of opinion that this change of direction was made deliberately so that the bridge might better resist the force of the current. In view of the fact that floods 15 feet deep are by no means unusual in the Rhône, this theory seems very plausible. The roadway over the bridge was 12 feet wide and was probably used only by horsemen, pack animals and foot passengers. There was a foolish tendency in those days to prohibit the passage of loaded coaches on the grounds of safety. On the Pont St Esprit a body of ruffianly porters used to insist on unloading all carriages and taking the goods over on low-wheeled trolleys, for which service they demanded excessive payment.[1] On a pier near the Avignon end of the bridge Bénézet built a chapel to the honour of St Nicholas, the patron saint of travellers. Here Bénézet was buried in 1184 and his tomb became a place of pilgrimage. When he died, work on the masterpiece he had created was well advanced and it was completed in 1187.

Two centuries later, for the sake of his own safety, Boniface IX destroyed one of the arches. This was repaired but so badly that it collapsed again and its failure resulted in the fall of five more spans. In 1670, the break up of ice in the river destroyed nearly the whole of the remainder.

*   *   *

Possibly the oldest of the surviving medieval bridges in France is that over the river Lot at Espalion. For years controversy has persisted as to the date of its construction. Some authorities maintain that it was built by the order of Charlemagne between the years 768 and 814 for use in the war against the Saracens in Spain. During his forty-five-year reign, Charlemagne did more than any other monarch to rescue roads and bridges from the decay into which they had relapsed. He not only created the toll system to pay for their maintenance but also saw to it that the work was done even if he had to resort to the labour of his troops on fatigue duty.

Thus there is little doubt that a bridge was built at Espalion in

[1] In Sikkim the author has seen baggage mules unloaded before crossing a timber cantilever bridge. The mules, however, were then hallooed over the bridge in a stampeding herd, imposing far greater strain on it than if the loaded baggage train had been led over quietly.

his time and the only point at issue is whether this is the one we see to-day or whether it was rebuilt in the twelfth or thirteenth century. On the one hand it is pointed out that the work is uncouth and far below the standard of the thirteenth century. On the other hand it is argued, although perhaps not very convincingly, that the bridge has pointed arches and that these could not have been introduced into France from the East before the return of the first Crusaders in the year 1110. A stronger argument perhaps is the resemblance of the bridge in form, though not in quality of

FIG. 10. The Devil's bridge over the river Serchio near Lucca.

workmanship, to the Pont Valentré, some 75 miles away, which was known to have been completed in 1308; and the similarity of certain other details to the Entraygues bridge over the Truyère, supposed to have been built subsequently to 1269.

However that may be, the original bridge had four very flat pointed arches, surmounted by three fortified towers. The arches, which are of unequal span, the longest being about 50 feet, spring from sturdy square piers founded on rock, which no doubt accounts for their survival. For in its endurance down the years, the bridge has been scarred, battered, and patched up like a veteran of the wars.

*   *   *

Perhaps the most extraordinary arch of medieval times is that of the Devil's bridge over the river Serchio near Lucca in Italy (Fig. 10). It was built by Castracini in 1317 on a site where it is thought that a Roman bridge previously carried the Via Capia, the road made by the Romans across the Apennines. The main arch is semi-circular; it springs directly from foundations in bedrock and has a span of 120 feet and a rise of exactly half that amount. The width of the bridge is only 12 feet and the roadway narrows from 11 feet at the ends to 9 feet at the crown. It is amazing that such a splendid lofty arch built only in stone should have survived a wild, torrential river like the Serchio for more than six centuries. During floods, the water rises to a depth of more than 30 feet, pouring over the approach arches at each end and making the roadway impassable. The arch stones are comparatively small, made of blue limestone and a variety of sandstone; the piers and spandrels are of rubble.

The survival of the bridge may be ascribed to the rock foundation and the excellent quality of its mortar for which Italy was rightly famed.

* * *

The Pont Valentré at Cahors (Pl. 3) is the most outstanding example of a medieval war-bridge that remains in France to-day. The town of Cahors is surrounded on three sides by the river Lot, which was crossed by bridges to the east and west. Of these only the western one, at the entrance to the valley, (hence its name 'Val-Entrée') is now surviving. When it was built between 1308 and 1355, by an architect whose name we do not know, the bridge formed an isolated advance defence post, at some distance from the town. It consists of six pointed arches of about 54-foot span, flanked by tall end towers, beyond each of which is another lesser arch. A third tower is provided for an outlook post in the middle of the bridge, all three towers rising to a height of about 116 feet above low water. The three stone towers standing high over the wide arches of the bridge dominate the scene like sentinels eternally on guard over the townsfolk of Cahors.

The roadway, which is not steeply hog-backed, is 16 feet wide except at the towers, where it is reduced to 10 feet or so. The piers, which are founded on rock, have long cutwaters upstream and short projections on the downstream face. Their walls rise straight up to a height a little above the crown of the arches and are protected by crenellated parapets. The first story of the three towers is reached by outside stairways sheltered by stepped battlements; interior wooden stairways lead to the upper stories. The two end towers are strongly fortified, nearly every possible defensive device being provided. On the ground floor are draw-bridges and heavy doors; on the first and second floors slits less than 2 inches wide for arrows and bolts; on the third floor machi-colations[1] for throwing down on the enemy stones or other missiles; on the topmost story are battlements with covered loopholes for long-range shooting. As there were also earthworks and fortifi-cations in front of both towers, it can be seen that the capture of the bridge in the days before artillery must have presented a tough proposition. Each of the piers is pierced by a transverse passage at the level of the arch springings, with rows of holes beneath it. Shaw Sparrow[2] points out how these openings were used to support the scaffolding when the bridge was built:

'The first stage was to thrust fir saplings through the holes in a pier till they jutted out on each side; then they were covered with planks and used as footbridges by the workmen, and also as resting-places for barrow-loads of dressed stones, which were lifted up by movable cranes. The service of the masons was effected through the bay in a pier, and the centering of every arch was in those other [i.e. the lower] holes.'

The bridge was built to the order of Raymond Panchelli, Bishop of Cahors, and financed by the revenues of the borough assisted by tolls and endowments. The toll was known as 'barres', after the counterweighted pole or bar erected at the gates, similar to that used on early turnpikes.

* * *

Another war-bridge famous in history is the Vieux Pont over the Gave-de-Pau at Orthez in the French Pyrénées (Fig. 11). The main arch of the bridge spans the river at its narrowest where it is hemmed between steep rocky banks. On each of the sturdy abutments was raised a tall fortified guard-tower, only one of which is now standing. On the right bank were built two or three smaller arches intended to increase the free waterway in times of flood. To connect the main span with the left bank a little timber bridge was provided which could easily be destroyed in time of

[1] A projecting parapet or gallery with openings in the floor.
[2] Frank Brangwyn and W. Shaw Sparrow, *A Book of Bridges*. 1920.

war. The roadway, which appears to have been widened more than once, is curved in line and of varying width. As at Cahors, it was flanked with high parapets to screen the defenders of the bridge and to enable them to move about unseen. The arches are pointed and of no great span; the main arch has an opening of only about 49 feet.

Probably built in the thirteenth century, the bridge has obviously been subjected to modifications and repair on many

FIG. 11. The old bridge at Orthez as it possibly appeared in the 16th century, showing the high parapets to screen the defenders, and the timber bridge on the right-hand side beyond the large arch. The bridge is shown like this in a design worked in needlework in 1589.

occasions. The single remaining tower has a machicolation so placed as to guard its base from attacks by boats or scaling ladders. Where the roadway passed through it in a vaulted passage, was a small aperture known as the Priest's Window. Through this opening the Huguenot soldiers of Queen Jeanne hurled the captured Catholic priests after the sacking of Orthez. The last occasion on which the bridge figured in military history was in February 1814 when Wellington defeated the French under Marshal Soult. According to Dartein, forty-five light infantrymen of Soult's rearguard, who were barricaded in the tower of the bridge, held off the attack of the English throughout the day. The bridge had apparently been mined by the French, but when the charge was exploded the stonework proved too solid for it and only the parapets were destroyed. The damage to the bridge was not all loss, however, as when the parapets were rebuilt the opportunity was taken to widen the roadway by corbelling it out on either side.

*   *   *

Communications are so vital in war that bridges have always been and still are of the first importance. In the second world war we have only to remember the opportunism of the American forces who captured the bridge over the Rhine at Remagen before it could be destroyed, and the gallant attack by the British 1st Airborne Division on the bridge at Arnhem[1]. One of the medieval bridges that played an important part in military history was the 'Auld Brig' at Stirling. In 1297 the Earl of Surrey ordered his troops across to attack the Scots under Sir William Wallace, but the bridge was so narrow that they could only cross two by two. When half the troops were across, Wallace, who was awaiting his opportunity, seized the bridge and then proceeded to 'mop up' the disorganized troops on either side. The old bridge is no longer standing but its successor, built at the end of the fourteenth century, is preserved as a monument to this day.

*   *   *

The building of the first stone bridge in London[2] was begun under the direction of Peter of Colechurch in 1176, the year before Bénézet started work on his far-famed Pont d'Avignon. But London bridge (Pl. 4) was a far more difficult proposition. It was the first bridge with masonry foundations to be built in a tidal waterway; the construction of these in the muddy bed of the river, with its swiftly flowing stream and tidal range of 16 feet, must have presented a tremendous problem. Stone had never been used on the site before and it had to be brought from a considerable distance. It was obvious that the cost of the bridge would be high, both in lives and money; and many years would be needed for its completion. According to John Stow the course

---

[1] Arnhem bridge was destroyed but replaced and opened in 1950.
[2] For the facts in this section, the Author is primarily indebted to Gordon Home's *Old London Bridge*.

of the river was temporarily diverted to assist in building the foundations. There is no other evidence of this, however, whereas examination of the piers when some were demolished in 1826-27 clearly indicated that they had been built inside timber coffer-dams. These were not made watertight and pumped dry in the modern manner, but served simply to hold the foundation stones in place.

Peter, the bridgemaster, was also chaplain of St Mary Cole-church, and had been in charge of the last of the numerous timber bridges that was built over the Thames in 1163. He appears to have been quite undaunted by the magnitude of his task; although he did not live to see the day, the completion of the bridge after thirty-three years of toil was doubtless due to his unwearying perseverance. For more than five centuries it was the only bridge over the Thames in London; during that time its charred and weatherbeaten stones carried all the cross-river traffic in what was soon to be the greatest city in the world.

The original design consisted of nineteen pointed arches and a drawbridge which was incorporated both for defence and to let ships pass at high water. It appears that the arches were intended to be of 28-foot span and the piers 20 feet wide; in practice, however, possibly owing to obstacles encountered in pile-driving, the spans of the arches, some of which were very flat, varied from 15 to 34 feet, and the widths of the piers from about 18 to 26 feet. Near the middle of the bridge was built a grand pier, larger than any of the others. This served the dual purpose of providing space for a chapel, built beside the roadway, and also acting as a massive buttress or anchorage in mid-river, to withstand the force of flood and the impact of ice and other perils. Gordon Home has given us a vivid picture of the building of the bridge:

'As pier after pier was added to the structure the difficulties produced by the great rush of water through the narrowing space left to it must have made the pile-driving and other work increasingly difficult and hazardous. It is in fact quite possible that some 250 lives were lost during the work. Year after year it continued, an arch being completed on the average every 18 months. The pile drivers, mounted no doubt on specially con-structed barges, would be an everyday sight, and loungers on the wooden bridge would have watched the slow winding up followed by the sudden drop of the heavy weights which inch by inch brought the pile down to the level of low water. They would have watched the hoisting of the blocks of stone from the barges, the difficulty of getting the lowest courses of masonry placed on the foundations just exposed at low tide, and the pouring in of hot pitch, and later on would have seen the carpenters fixing their wooden centering upon which were placed the carefully shaped voussoirs of the arch stones.'

The severe constriction of the waterway, however, produced a new danger. The width of the river of about 900 feet was nearly halved by the width of the piers (Fig. 12). At the base of each pier was a wide 'starling', consisting of stone pitching enclosed by piles, the size of which grew with every repair. Thus at half tide the waterway was reduced to less than 250 feet and moreover the flow was subsequently further obstructed by water wheels in one or more of the arches. The effect of all this was to close five-sixths of the river channel and so dam up the water that both on the ebb and flow the tide roared through the narrow openings like a mill race. In effect a weir was created, with a maximum head of 5 feet which made navigation beneath the bridge a highly perilous adventure. Hence the old saying that 'London Bridge is intended for wise men to go over and fools to go under'. The width of the roadway was originally 20 feet overall and its height only about 32 feet above low water. There was thus little enough headroom below the arches on the flood tide.

The bridge was finally completed in 1209, and Peter of Cole-church, who had supported the burden of the work for twenty-nine years, died before the last few arches were finished. He was buried in the undercroft of the bridge chapel, amidst the sights and sounds of the port of London that he knew so well. King John had suggested to the mayor and citizens of London that the Frenchman Isembert, who had recently built bridges at Saintes and La Rochelle, should be asked to finish the work. But according to John Stow, it was completed by three 'worthy merchants of London, Serle Mercer, William Almaine, and Benedict Bote-write', whom he calls 'principall Meisters of that worke'. He makes no mention of Isembert and it seems very doubtful whether he had anything to do with it.

The funds for the building of the bridge came from both national and private sources. In addition to endowments and generous individual subscriptions, chiefly from dignitaries of the church, revenue was forthcoming from a special tax on wool imposed by Henry II. Hence the oft-repeated tale that the foundations of the bridge were laid on woolpacks. The cost of building the bridge chapel was borne by the master mason, who was a mayor of London. Could any clearer sign be needed of the pride that such craftsmen took in their work? The bridge was most efficiently protected by means of the Stone Gate near the south end, then the drawbridge, and then a second gate beyond it to the north. With such defences and resolute men to man them, it is small wonder that no attack on the bridge ever succeeded. The heads of men who attempted it, such as Thomas Fauconberg, leader of the men of Kent, in 1471, were subsequently displayed with those of traitors on poles above the drawbridge gate.

The fame of old London bridge, however, probably rests chiefly on its street of houses and shops, the rents from which were intended, with the help of tolls, to pay for its upkeep. These shops fronted on the narrow roadway, reducing its width to 12 feet; at the back they overhung the river and were supported on great timber struts. Their upper floors projected and overhung the street; some were even built to bridge the full width of the road. With access further reduced by stalls in front of the shops, the scene of congestion in the narrow tunnel of the bridge, thronged with carts, horsemen, cattle and pedestrians, defies imagination. Accidents were frequent and fires an all too common occurrence.

A few years after the bridge was finished, in July 1212, a terrible fire swept it from end to end. The wooden buildings and their contents roared up in flames, so swiftly that thousands of citizens were trapped and many lost their lives, some in the river where they leapt for safety and others in the conflagration. Episodes like this, however, seem to have been little setback to the tough, virile Londoners. The rows of shops and houses were rebuilt and made more commodious and substantial than before. Cellars were constructed within and between the bridge piers. Little gardens with arbours were laid out and platforms built on the roofs whereon the tenants could walk and enjoy the fine prospect up and down the river. Centuries later came the Great Fire of 1666 when the city side of London bridge[1] was ravaged, and even the mighty tower of St Pauls came down in splintered masonry and flame.

> And shepherds from the lonely height
> Of Hampstead gazing down
> Saw heaving in a lake of light
> The heart of London town.

[1] The fire did not spread right across the bridge because there was a gap in the buildings caused by a fire in 1632.

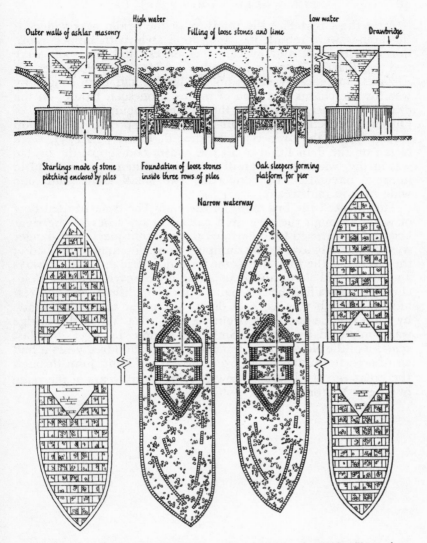

Outer walls of ashlar masonry

High water

Filling of loose stones and lime

Low water

Drawbridge

Starlings made of stone pitching enclosed by piles

Foundation of loose stones inside three rows of piles

Oak sleepers forming platform for pier

Narrow waterway

FIG. 12. An elevation and plan of a few spans of Old London bridge illustrating the foundations, piers and arches; the centre part of the drawing indicates the internal construction. The piers and arches are shown before the 18th century alterations, and are those which carry the large block of houses in the centre of John Varley's watercolour drawing reproduced in Plate 4. The details are largely based on drawings made by William Knight and E. W. Cooke during the demolition of the bridge between 1826 and 1831.

After the Great Fire the roadway of the bridge was widened; the houses were rebuilt in Restoration style with hipped roofs, dormer windows, and overhanging eaves; and the roofs were tied together at intervals by timber arches across the street. In Elizabethan times dwellings on the bridge had been sought by wealthy merchants and men of means. Nonesuch House, on the drawbridge pier, had been the home of young noblemen of Queen Elizabeth's court. But as London spread, the fashion changed, and the property deteriorated. Finally, in 1757, work began on the demolition of all the houses and shops; the bridge was further widened and an ill considered scheme put in hand to improve navigation by converting two small arches into one wide span in midstream.

This marked the beginning of the end. The concentrated flow of water through the new arch caused heavy scour of the river bed and threatened to undermine the adjacent piers. The danger was temporarily averted by dumping stone pitching on the bed of the river, but the time had come for a new bridge. The gateways and all the old shops and houses had gone, seven of Peter Colechurch's arches had been rebuilt, three demolished, and the rest hidden beneath new work. A design for a new bridge was made by John Rennie and work begun on it in 1824. When this bridge was completed by his son Sir John Rennie in 1831, the last remains of the old one were removed. For six hundred years it had weathered storm and flood, from the days of King John through the great age of Elizabeth, down to within six years of the reign of Queen Victoria.

Chapter 5

BIRTH OF
THE MODERN BRIDGE

'Bid harbours open, public ways extend;
Bid temples worthier of God ascend;
Bid the broad arch the dang'rous flood contain. . . .'

POPE

THE RENAISSANCE—that great upsurge of interest in art and
science and sudden zest to live life to its full—had its origin in
Florence in the fifteenth century. It was born out of the vision of
men in the tradition of Leonardo da Vinci;[1] manifested in the
paintings and sculpture of Michelangelo and Donatello; proclaimed in the writings of Dante; and reached its architectural
perfection in the works of Palladio and Vignola. Amongst bridges
it was responsible for the finest achievements of the sixteenth
century—the sturdy Pont Notre Dame and Pont Neuf in Paris,
the lovely Santa Trinita bridge in Florence itself and the picturesque Rialto bridge spanning the Grand Canal in Venice.

Following on this re-awakening of spirit and energy, bridge-
building in the seventeenth and eighteenth centuries at last
became a science. Lines of thrust were plotted, the strength of
materials and foundations closely estimated. In 1716 was formed
the Corps des Ingénieurs des Ponts et Chaussées, the members of
which were engineers trained in Paris, to whom plans of all
roads, bridges, and canals in central France had to be submitted
for approval. Some years later they founded the first engineering
school in the world, to which Jean Perronet was appointed
Director. By the middle of the eighteenth century, bridge building
in masonry reached its zenith in such masterpieces as Perronet's
bridge at Neuilly and William Edwards's at Pontypridd. By this
time, as we shall see, bridge trusses[2] of timber, first evolved by

---

[1] See Note on p. 62.

[2] A truss is a framed or jointed structure designed to act as a beam, while each
member is usually subjected to longitudinal stress only, either tension or compression.

Palladio, had been developed by the brothers Grubenmann in Switzerland. Their use continued, particularly in North America, until late in the nineteenth century. But long before that the first iron bridge had been built in England and a new age had begun.

Let us first see the effect of the Renaissance on the bridges in France. In the days when Paris, or Lutetia as it was then called, was the headquarters of the Roman occupation, it was confined to the island in the Seine now known as La Cité. Under Julius Caesar, and even up to the fourth century A.D., there was only one river crossing; this was provided by two timber bridges, which linked the island to the river banks. Ten centuries passed before the increase in traffic led to the building of the first Pont Notre Dame, so called because it gave direct access to the cathedral. Sixty houses were built on the bridge, which was of timber, and Charles VI conceded the rents from them to the city authorities for its maintenance. In spite of many cajolings and warnings, however, no repairs were made, and in 1499 the whole structure collapsed into the river. By this time the Renaissance had spread to Paris, and under its stimulus the decision was made to rebuild the bridge in stone. The requisite funds were raised by means of a toll on cattle, fish, and salt.

The work was entrusted to Fra Giovanni Giocondo, who on account of his fame in both science and the arts, had been invited to Paris to advise Charles VIII on the Italian style in building. Giocondo had restored the old Roman bridge at Verona and was subsequently engaged on the strengthening of the foundations of St Peter's in Rome.

The Pont Notre Dame consisted of six arches, the central four having spans of 57 feet. Discussion arose as to whether the foundations should be excavated to bed rock or whether they should be piled. This was one of numerous disputes between Giocondo and Didier de Félin, one of the French superintendents, in which Giocondo usually seemed to get his way. Piles consisting of heavy tree trunks were finally adopted and they were driven inside cofferdams from which the water had been expelled by means of horse-operated pumps. The masonry piers were then built in the dry on footings of rubble concrete.

The bridge was completed in 1507, after seven years' work, and two fine rows of four-story houses with cellars were built lining the roadway. Although the backs of the houses overhung the river, they reduced the width of highway available for traffic from 75 feet to 25 feet, which was evidently considered sufficient at that time. The roadway must have been in a foul condition,

as it sloped down from either side to a single central gutter
provided for refuse and drainage. It was not until 1786 that the
volume of traffic brought about the demolition of the houses, and
the roadway was rebuilt 42 feet wide with footways and parapets
on either side. In spite of the designer's efforts to avoid scour
around the piers by leaving as wide a waterway as possible, the
city authorities installed a weir beneath one arch and mills under
two others. When the old arches were demolished in 1853,
however, their foundations were found to be in such good condition, after 350 years, that they were built into the new bridge
that we see to-day.

*   *   *

The second great Renaissance bridge in Paris is the famous Pont
Neuf built in 1578-1604 to the order of Henry III at the downstream end of the Île de la Cité. The north and south parts of the
bridge consist of seven and five spans respectively; the arches are
all built on a slight skew, and vary in span from 32 to 64 feet; the
piers also vary in thickness. The roadway was 66 feet wide with
footways raised two steps above it on either side.

The bridge was designed by Jacques Androuet du Cerceau but
the commissioners appointed a board of experts, consisting of
master carpenters, master masons, and others to advise on the design
and execution of the work. One of the first things to decide was the
type of foundation. The three methods then in use were to place
the ashlar foundation stones a) directly on the subsoil, b) on a
timber grillage, c) on timber piles. In spite of the fact that an
extra depth of only ten feet would have reached the underlying
rock, the board decided to lay the masonry on grillages of timber.
Only one of them, Lescot, appears to have had doubts about the
quality of the subsoil and would have preferred to use piles. The
piers were built inside timber cofferdams, which were driven to
refusal by means of a mechanical pile driver. After pumping the
cofferdams out and excavating the soft subsoil, a timber grillage
was laid down, on top of which the masonry was built. In spite of
the expert's advice, in a few years two of the piers were so badly
undermined by scour that they had to be reconstructed even
before the bridge was finished. To do this another cofferdam was
built round the upstream end of the piers, inside which the original
work was repaired. Permanent sheet piling was then driven close
against the walls of the piers and anchored to them by iron ties to
protect the base against scour. The absence of bearing piles

below the foundations proved a permanent weakness, however, and repairs had to be carried out due to settlement on several subsequent occasions.

The building of the superstructure presented no unusual problems, although it was found many years later that parts of the work had been scamped, and that some of the arches were less than the specified thickness. The bridge was opened in 1605 and at once established itself as the main artery of the city. For more than 200 years it was one of the busiest and liveliest centres of Paris. Between the rows of little shops flanking the roadway flowed a ceaseless stream of the city traffic—carts, horsemen, carriages, sedan chairs. The narrow footpaths, lined with market stalls, were thronged with people of every class and profession. Priests and shopkeepers rubbed shoulders with lackeys, artisans, and sailors; and amongst the honest citizens of Paris mingled loafers, cloak-snatchers, and pickpockets awaiting their opportunity. So serious did the nuisance become that in 1640 an Act was passed forbidding 'lackeys, soldiers, vagabonds and all others playing cards, dice, or other forbidden games on the Pont Neuf'. During the Revolution, carts rumbled continually across the bridge carrying victims to the guillotine.

In 1848 an extensive reconstruction of the whole bridge was carried out. Flatter elliptical arches were built in place of the original circular ones on the north side, in order to reduce the rise and hence the gradient for traffic. The roadway was remodelled, the round shoulders on the pier ends were rebuilt all at the same height above the water, and ornamental parapets and lighting standards added.

*   *   *

At the time of the Renaissance one of the four medieval bridges over the Arno in Florence was the picturesque Ponte Vecchio (1367), lined with its famous goldsmith's shops; this bridge still stands to-day, little altered since the time of the Medici. Another was the Santa Trinita bridge which Cosimo I, the Grand Duke, ordered his engineer, Bartolomeo Ammanati, to replace (Pl. 5). Ammanati had studied under Sansovino, who made a design for the Rialto bridge in Venice and had completed the building of the Pitti Palace in Florence. The river was 320 feet wide at the site and Ammanati designed a most beautiful bridge of three arches, with spans of 87 feet, 96 feet, and 86 feet, respectively.

Possibly influenced by the Ponte Vecchio, which had excep-

1. The Alcantara bridge over the Tagus, built by the Roman, Caius Julius Lacer, for the Emperor Trajan and still standing after nearly 2,000 years.

2. The Pont du Gard, the famous Roman aqueduct near Nîmes.

The Pont Valentré at Cahors, a great medieval war bridge. Note the defences, including arrow slits, machicolations, and the protected stairway to the towers.

4. Old London Bridge c. 1750, from a watercolour drawing signed J. Varley, in the British Museum. Note the irregularity of the arches,

Bartolomeo Ammanati's famous Santa Trinita bridge at Florence, which was destroyed by German mines in the second world war.

6. The Britannia tubular bridge built by Robert Stephenson and William Fairbairn 1846-50, the forerunner of the modern plate girder. One of the spans is being floated out prior to jacking up to its final level.

7. The Royal Albert bridge at Saltash, Brunel's last and greatest work, 1855-59. The second span is being raised into position. Note the oval section of the curved upper chord and the suspension chains below.

8. Telford's Menai suspension bridge under reconstruction in 1940, after 125 years' us[e]
The original wrought-iron chains were completely replaced without interruptio[n]
of traffic.

9. The St. Louis bridge completed in 1874. The bridge is double-decked, and carries roadway traffic on the upper deck and two railway tracks below.

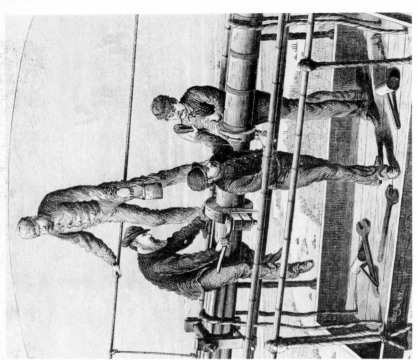

11. Compacting and binding the cables of the Brooklyn bridge.

10. The excavation shaft in the working chamber of the Brooklyn bridge caisson. The bottom of the shaft was kept sealed in a pit full of water; excavated rock was tipped into the pit, thrust beneath the shaft, and grabbed out from above. Note the use of candles for illumination.

12. and 13. ABOVE. The floating crane on the Storstrøm bridge carrying one of the side spans weighing 500 tons. The span, with a derrick on it, was placed on the piers 90 feet above water level. BELOW. The erection of the Vila Franca bridge over the Tagus (1951). Each span was erected in turn on a service girder, seen in the photograph, after being floated into position for erection of the fourth span.

14. Floating in one of the spans of the Hawkesbury River railway bridge, N.S. Wales (1946). The span is 445 feet

16. The wreckage of the Bandara bridge in Siam, destroyed by Allied bombs. This bridge has now been replaced by British engineers.

15. The Ava bridge over the Irrawaddy river. Two spans were blown to prevent the Japanese using the bridge in the 1939-45 war.

17. The Tavanasa bridge, one of the early three-hinged arches by Robert Maillart, the famous Swiss designer in reinforced concrete. Note the use of slabs and the fusion of deck and ribs.

18. Maillart's Schwandbach bridge, a stiffened slab arch, curved in plan; it carries a roadway on a hairpin bend across a deep ravine.

19. The new Waterloo bridge has a simplicity, cleanness of line, and absence of decoration unique on the Thames.

o and 21. ABOVE. The erection of the Sandö bridge in Sweden. The photograph shows
e timber staging being dismantled after the concreting of the arch rib. BELOW. The
ndö bridge, completed in 1943, is the longest reinforced concrete span in the world.

22. The massive cantilevers of the Forth bridge, shown under erection, were conceived in the shadow of the Tay bridge disaster.

23 and 24. ABOVE. Loss of the suspended span of the Quebec bridge in 1916. The span was 640 feet long and weighed 5,000 tons; its loss during hoisting was due to the failure of a casting. BELOW. Within a year a new span had been built and was successfully erected.

25. The erection of the Esbly pre-stressed concrete bridge over the river Marne. Not
the holes for the wires in the end of the lower flanges of the pre-cast unit, which i
being hoisted into position.

26 and 27. ABOVE. Erecting the high-tensile steel ribs of the Rainbow bridge at Niagara. Note the temporary anchorage cables and the safety nets suspended closely beneath the ribs. BELOW. The erection of the Birchenough bridge over the Sabi river in S. Rhodesia. In the distance is Mount Rudd, named after one of Cecil Rhodes's pioneers.

30. Making the end connection of the chord.

28. Preparations for applying compressed air to one of the wells of the Calcutta monolith of the new Howrah bridge. The heavy steel diaphragm is to be lowered into the well to form a roof to the

29. Erecting a 65-ton upper chord member. Note the crane hook and the ends of the members, in the top left and bottom right-hand corners of the photograph, to which the chord is to be connected.

31 and 32. ABOVE. Twelve of the fourteen panels on the south side of Sydney Harbour bridge, jutting out a distance of 700 feet over the harbour, weighing more than 12,000 tons, and held only by a temporary anchorage to the shore. BELOW. The temporary anchorage cables being removed after the two half arches of Sydney Harbour bridge had met and joined. 128 cables, each 2¾ inches in diameter, were connected here, at the ends of the upper chords.

33. Cable-spinning by night on the Bay Bridge at San Francisco. The cables were erected by double-sheaved spinning wheels that placed 128 tons of wire per day.

34. Diagrammatic view of the central anchorage of the twin suspension spans of the Bay bridge. The caisson was built up of 55 steel cylinders and was founded more than 200 feet below water level.

5.   Erection of the deck and stiffening trusses of the Bay bridge; units weighing up to 204
ons were floated out and lifted by cranes suspended immediately below the main cables.

36. The twin suspension spans of the Bay bridge opened to traffic in 1936. Although the bridge is double-decked it is already crowded to capacity, and there is a project to build another.

and 38. ABOVE. O. H. Ammann's mighty George Washington bridge over the Hudson
ver, New York. At one stroke this bridge practically doubled the maximum single span.
LOW. The compaction of the 3-ft.-diameter cables of the George Washington bridge
f. Pl. 11 showing the same process on the Brooklyn bridge). Each cable of the George
Washington bridge is built up of 26,474 parallel wires.

39.   The collapse of the deck of the Tacoma bridge in a wind of 42 m.p.h. four mont
after the bridge was opened in 1940. The disaster brought the new science of aerodynami
as applied to bridges urgently to the fore.

and 41. ABOVE. The swaying and oscillation of the deck under the action of quite moderate winds caused the Tacoma Narrows bridge to be nicknamed "Galloping Gertie." Low. The New Tacoma Narrows bridge completed in October 1950. Note the deep lattice stiffening truss in place of the shallow plate girder. In the background are the city of Tacoma and Mount Rainier.

42 and 43. ABOVE. The 4,200-ft. span of the Golden Gate bridge is the longest in the world to-day; it was opened in 1937. BELOW. Diagrammatic view showing the construction of the deep south pier of the Golden Gate bridge, virtually in the open sea.

tionally low arches for a medieval bridge, Ammanati designed those of Santa Trinita with a rise:span ratio of only 1 to 7 instead of the usual ratio of 1 to 4. He thus avoided a hog-backed road with its steeply inclined approaches, difficult for traffic to negotiate. Furthermore, in order to avoid the apparent weakness of a long flat soffit,[1] he had the courage to adopt the pointed arch of the East—and introduce it into the very home and citadel of the Roman circular arch. By two more strokes of genius he concealed the angle at the crown with carved pendants; and closely integrated arches and piers by starting the curves of the arches vertically from the springings. In effect Ammanati evolved the first 'basket-handled' arch—a shape that gives so many advantages that it has since been widely used. It was too much, of course, to expect popular opinion to accept such changes without suspicion. In fact it is said that not until after Napoleon had ordered his heavy artillery across the bridge, during his invasion of Italy, did other vehicles dare to use it!

The foundations were built inside cofferdams of an unusually extensive kind. Two concrete walls, 7 feet thick and about 90 feet apart, were built inside sheet piling right across the river, which was presumably diverted first to one side and then to the other. Cross walls were then built between them, thus forming rectangular cofferdams, which could be pumped out in turn, around the site of each pier. The ground inside was excavated to a depth of 13 feet and piled. The foundation stones of the piers, each measuring 6 feet × 18 inches in plan, were placed on the bearing piles and the masonry brought up to its full height. The arches were then built on seven temporary timber centres spaced 10 feet apart.

*　　*　　*

Ruskin described the famous Rialto bridge in Venice as 'the best building raised in the time of the Grotesque Renaissance; very noble in its simplicity, in its proportions and in its masonry'. Its low circular arch crosses the Grand Canal in a span of 88 feet, causing scarcely any interference with the waterway. The rise of the arch is only 21 feet, which allowed sufficient headroom for the state barges and galleys that used the canal when the bridge was built, and is ample to-day for the gondolas and motor launches that ply beneath it. The bridge is 75 feet wide and carries a central roadway lined with shops and sidewalks. There is, of

[1] The underside of an arch.

course, no wheeled traffic in Venice, and wide shallow steps carry
the roadway up over the rise of the arch (Fig. 13).

Since the twelfth century there had been a succession of bridges
on the site; these were of various kinds, including pontoon and
timber bridges and an ingenious bridge with a central opening
span that had two arms which could be raised like drawbridges to
let shipping pass. After a great fire in 1512, which ravaged the
Rialto district and threatened the bridge, Giocondo, who had
returned to live in Venice, suggested that a stone bridge should be
built with shops, as on the Pont Notre Dame.

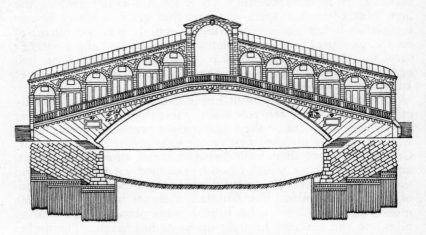

FIG. 13. The Rialto bridge showing, below water level, a section through the
foundations, drawn in accordance with da Ponte's description and a contemporary drawing by Giacomo Guberni, 'Master of the Waterfront' at Venice.

In the following years a number of eminent men, including
Michelangelo, Palladio, Scamozzi, and da Ponte prepared
designs; but of those that have survived, only that of Antonio da
Ponte, which was accepted in 1588, was suited to the site conditions and satisfactorily solved the difficult problem of the
foundations. For Venice is a city of many islands formed in soft
alluvial ground; not at all an easy subsoil in which to resist the
thrust of a low arch, surcharged with the weight of a street of
shops. Da Ponte solved the problem by means of extensive piling.
He drove as many as 6,000 piles of birch-alder beneath each abutment. The piles were 6 inches or so in diameter, 11 feet long, and
driven to refusal. Owing to the close proximity of buildings with

shallow foundations, he did not dare excavate to any great depth at the back of the abutments, but formed the ground into steps at three levels, the deepest of which was 16 feet at the canal front. These excavations were made inside cofferdams which were kept reasonably dry by means of large pumps. In order to get 6,000 piles in the base of each abutment they must have been driven so close .that they were practically touching each other. This would not be considered good practice to-day, but it appears to have been effective.

After driving, the pile heads were cut level and capped with three layers of timbers secured by iron clamps. Da Ponte then had wedge-shaped stones with brick backing laid on the timbers, in an endeavour to make the bed joints in the abutment normal to the line of thrust of the arch. This was an outstanding innovation that has frequently been adopted since da Ponte's day. In the great concrete skewbacks beneath the bearings of Sydney Harbour bridge, for instance, the concrete was so placed that every layer presented a number of facets approximately normal to the line of thrust of the arch.

Possibly owing to the envy of Scamozzi, whose design for a bridge on a widespread 'floating' foundation had been passed over in favour of da Ponte's piled abutments, construction was not allowed to proceed unhindered. Work was halted while a lengthy enquiry was held into the correctness and adequacy of the project. A great number of witnesses were heard, including da Ponte himself, who presented an admirably clear and logical argument in support of his design. In the outcome, the commission accepted all his proposals and the work was completed in accordance with his plans. A few years after it was opened the bridge was shaken by an earthquake that rocked the city. Shopkeepers fled in terror, only to return after the rumbling and quaking of the ground had ceased, to find the bridge intact and with no sign of injury.

So it stands to this day, with its busy markets at either end, still the main crossing of the canal and daily thronged with the life and bustle of the city. Venice owes much besides the Rialto bridge to Antonio da Ponte. On two occasions in his capacity as curator of public works he saved the Doge's Palace from serious damage by fire, fearlessly entering the blazing building and directing the firefighters. In 1589 he rebuilt the prison, and is responsible for the poignant Bridge of Sighs, over which prisoners were taken for trial in the Palace.

*   *   *

The Pont Royal built in Paris towards the end of the seventeenth century may be regarded as the first modern masonry bridge. It was built solely as a bridge, for the purpose of providing a wide roadway for traffic, with as little obstruction as possible of the river. No houses were built on it; the road and footways were kept clear and unencumbered.

The design was made by Jules-Hardouin Mansard and the construction directed by Jacques (IV) Gabriel, Louis XIV's architect, who had played a large part in the building of the Palace of Versailles. When Gabriel died some months after the commencement of the work, the responsibility for its completion devolved on his widow, Marie de Lisle. Fortunately her brother Pierre, another architect to the king, was able to take over and direct the work on her behalf.

The bridge has five 'basket-handled' arches varying in span from 64 to 72 feet, springing from piers about 14 feet thick. The roadway is 55 feet wide inclusive of footways and parapets. Before work started, a comprehensive specification was drawn up stating exactly how the bridge was to be built, the quality of materials to be used, and the estimated cost, which was to be borne by the king. The use of cofferdams was specified for the construction of the foundations; their walls were to be made 9 feet thick, and to consist of clay puddle between a double sheathing of timbers. The cofferdams were to be pumped out and the ground excavated to a depth of 15 feet below low water. Timber bearing piles 10 inches to 12 inches in diameter were to be driven at 18-inch centres over the area of the base of each pier. The pile heads were to be cut level and capped with a timber platform on which the masonry of the pier was built. The kind of stone to be used in every part of the work was specified:

'The builders will use: the hard stone of Saint-Cloud below low water; the hard stone of Bagneux for the piers up to the springings of the arches and for the spandrels, coping, parapets and kerbs; Vergelé stone for the body of the arches; Vaugirard rubble-stones for filling the piers and abutments.'

The result of collaboration between Mansard, a skilled architect, and Friar Romain, who was general inspector of the works, the bridge was long in advance of its time and served as a model, particularly in its foundations, for many years.

*   *   *

The next advance was made by Jean Perronet (1708-94) who had been impressed by the proportions of bridges in China, in which the roadway was carried by huge stone slabs on vertical piers. This gave Perronet the idea of building very flat arches, supported on piers that were simply designed to carry their weight, the whole of the horizontal thrust being transmitted through the arches to the abutments at each end. Incidentally anchorage at the ends is one of the methods adopted in the design of earthquake-proof bridges to-day. It enabled Perronet to reduce

FIG. 14. The building of Neuilly bridge as shown in contemporary engravings. In the left centre the masonry of one of the piers has almost reached the level of the capping stones, one of which is being hauled off the wagon in the foreground. The timber centerings for the arches are seen, each loaded with rows of stones at the top to counterbalance the thrust of the arch stones already in place at the springings. Two timber service bridges flank the structure, and on the far one, in the centre background, is seen a large wheel used for lifting heavy loads.

the thickness of the river piers and so leave a wider waterway for traffic and lessen the risk of scour; at the same time it opened the way for flatter arches with comparatively high springings. It was essential, however, that the spans should be almost equal, so as to avoid unbalanced thrust on the piers, and that all the arches should be built before the temporary centering in any one of them was removed. Perronet was confirmed in these ideas by his experience on the bridge at Mantes, designed by M. Hupeaux, which he completed in 1765. Here the ratio of thickness of piers to span of arch was 1:5; but when one of the side spans was almost finished and the central span only just begun, the unbalanced thrust pushed the intermediate pier over 5 inches sideways. Perronet decided that if it was necessary to make the piers thicker than this, to enable each arch to be self-supporting, the obstruction to the waterway would be so great that it was much better to make the arches rely one on another and to carry the horizontal thrust through to the abutment. In his bridges, therefore, he reduced the thickness of the piers to as little as 1/10 of the span. Subsequently, however, he advised the Government that abutment piers should be provided at distances of three to four arches apart in long bridges. This would not only be more

FIG. 15. Neuilly bridge completed. The arches are splayed out at the piers in what are known as 'cornes de vache'.

economical in erection, but would prevent all the other arches collapsing following the destruction of one of them. It is of interest to note that Jacques (V) Gabriel had designed two abutment piers of this kind in his bridge of eleven arches over the Loire at Blois built in 1716-24; but the idea was never generally adopted.

In the Neuilly bridge over the Seine, Perronet reduced the thickness of the piers to less than 1/9 of the span of the arches (Figs. 14 and 15). This became a matter of hot debate at the Assemblée des Ingénieurs des Ponts et Chaussées but unfortunately there is no record of the proceedings. Even after the bridge had been

finished a certain engineer, M. Defer, expressed such concern for
its safety that he asked for sentinels to be placed at the ends of the
bridge to slow down the speed of carriages and for the roadway
to be covered with 4-inch thick matting to damp out the impact
of the wheels on the paving stones!

The striking of the arch centres was an event probably unique
in bridge building:

'The King having expressed a wish to witness the final operations
of de-centering, a site was prepared where there were set up a
tent for His Majesty, one for the princes, one for the ambassadors,
one for the lords of the court and the ministers, and others for the
public. It was arranged that the centering of the arches should
fall consecutively, within a few minutes. Two winches with ropes
were set up to the right of each arch and nine men put to each
winch. In $3\frac{1}{2}$ minutes all the staging had fallen away. When it
fell, the mass of timber caused the spray to fly as high as the top
of the bridge. His Majesty expressed his satisfaction and on his
way back to Marly drove over the bridge in his carriage.'

Dinner was provided for the spectators and a medal was struck
to commemorate the event. Shaw Sparrow points out, however,
that the centering was removed much too soon—only eighteen
days after the keystones of the arches had been placed and before
the mortar had sufficiently hardened. To this he ascribes the
settlement of 23 inches that took place at the crown of one of the
arches and considers that Perronet's reputation was saved 'not by
his good design, nor by his mathematical calculations, but by a
rare stroke of good luck'! Perhaps such strokes of luck are not so
rare.

Many judges consider that the Pont Sainte-Maxence over the
Oise is Perronet's finest work. Here the arches are flatter, the
piers even more slender, and the waterway less obstructed than at
Neuilly. Perronet further reduced the volume of the piers by
omitting the stonework in the centre, so that the arches appear to
spring from pairs of coupled columns. Perronet's last work was the
Pont de la Concorde (1787-91). Unfortunately the authorities
insisted on the piers being made solid, and the rise of the arches
being increased by three feet to give more headroom for shipping.
These modifications must have been galling to an engineer of
such eminence, and they prevent us from seeing the bridge as
Perronet designed it. Nevertheless, it is a beautiful bridge. A
critic forty years later referred to the central arch as 'the most

daring construction that has yet been executed'. Perronet watched
the bridge being built from a little pavilion at one end; here he
saw the first stone set in place and here he died after the work
had been finished.

*   *   *

In London the need was felt for another bridge over the Thames
to ease the congestion on Old London bridge. Its construction
was opposed for years, but finally Parliament decided to build a
bridge at Westminster and to pay for it out of the proceeds of a
public lottery! The work was entrusted to a young Swiss engineer,
Labelye, and was begun in 1738. A novel method was used for
building the foundations. This consisted of floating out a huge
timber box, or 'chest', measuring 80 feet by 30 feet overall in
plan. The base of the box was a solid timber grillage and the sides
were detachable and sufficiently high to stand above water level
when the chest was sunk. By opening a sluice gate at the bottom,
the chest could be flooded and sunk; by closing the sluice valve
and pumping out the water it could be floated up again, if desired.
After excavating the site of the pier about 6 feet deep, the chest
was sunk in position with several courses of masonry built inside
it. The sides of the chest were then removed and used for the next
pier, the base remaining permanently in the foundation. This idea
might well have been successful if the subsoil had been strong
enough to stand without piling, and if precautions had been
taken to prevent the foundation from being undermined by
scour. At Westminster no bearing piles were driven nor any other
precaution taken, and serious settlement of the piers resulted; it is
perhaps surprising therefore that the bridge survived for a hundred
years.

It was not until the turn of the century that John Rennie
(1761-1821) upon whom Perronet's mantle fell, built the Waterloo, Southwark, and new London bridges. There was nothing new
in the foundations of these bridges, which consisted of timber rafts
on bearing piles. As regards the superstructure, old Waterloo
bridge was much the most attractive, as witness the outcry that
arose some years ago when the L.C.C. announced their intention
of pulling it down. Both Waterloo and the new London bridge
consisted of multiple masonry arches, the biggest spans in each
being 119 feet and 152 feet respectively. Old Southwark bridge,
commenced in 1815, consisted of three cast-iron arches, the central
one having a span of 240 feet.   Of these three bridges only London

bridge has survived to the present day. Perhaps the most extraordinary thing about it is its great cost of £1,458,311—an immense
sum in those days for a multi-span bridge little more than 1,000
feet long. In addition to his fame as a bridge builder Rennie had
made a reputation for himself in successfully draining and
reclaiming marshes in the eastern counties and in building a
number of harbours and docks including the London dock and
East India dock on the Thames.

*   *   *

Before closing this chapter we must refer to an outstanding
example of intuitive skill in construction shown by two village
carpenters, Ulric and Jean Grubenmann of Teufen, Switzerland.
Their most famous work was the covered timber bridge over the
Rhine at Schaffhausen built in 1755-58 (Fig. 16). This bridge

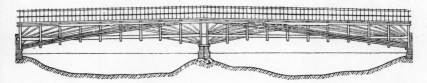

FIG. 16. The Grubenmann brothers' bridge at Schaffhausen, with the external
planking removed to show the construction.

had two spans of 193 and 171 feet respectively, which formed an
elbow pointing upstream. Ulric had proposed to build a single
span across the river, but the town magistrates insisted that he
should make use of a remaining pier in midstream. The bridge
was completely successful and cost only £8,000; unfortunately it
was burnt by French troops when they evacuated Schaffhausen
after being defeated by the Austrians, in 1799. Telford made a
report on the bridge in which he agreed that if it had been built
straight across the river it might well have stood as a single span.
     Before the work was finished, Jean Grubenmann built a similar
timber bridge of 240 feet span at Reichenau. By this time the
fame of the brothers Grubenmann had travelled to North
America, where a great variety of timber truss bridges were
evolved. Foremost among the designers of these were Theodore
Burr, Louis Wernwag, who built the Colossus bridge of 340-foot
span over the Schuylkill river, and William Howe. The majority
of the designs were indeterminate, however, in that they com-

bined arch and truss systems; the most satisfactory was the Howe truss, a purely lattice bridge with vertical iron ties, which was largely used in the early railroads. Although it has many valuable properties, however, timber is not a suitable material for permanent bridgework and would not be used in work of importance to-day.

Note (see p. 49). According to Dr. F. Stüssi of Zurich, in a brochure just published, Leonardo da Vinci wrote to Sultan Bajezid II in 1502-3 offering to build him windmills, pumps and bridges, including a masonry arch bridge over the Golden Horn with a span of 276 m. (905 feet). Dr. Stüssi has investigated Leonardo's design and found it to be stable and sound, but he does not believe that the bridge could have been built in those days, on account of the difficulty of supporting the arch centering. Incidentally, no masonry, brick, or even reinforced concrete arch has yet been built of such a span! (May, 1953).

Chapter 6

THE RINGING
GROOVES OF CHANGE

'By the eighteenth century Britain was more closely
unified by roads than it had been since Roman times
and soon this was reinforced by the canals, a quiet,
deliberate form of carriage that came to have its own
nomadic population. Then down the ringing grooves of
change came the railway engine begotten by Watt and
Stephenson on the iron-and-coal age.'

JACQUETTA HAWKES, *A Land*, 1951

BEFORE THE industrial revolution in England, transport had been
restricted to horse-drawn vehicles, sailing vessels, and canal boats;
materials of construction were limited to wood, brick, and stone.
Then, as iron began to supplement wood and stone, bridge
builders had a new material to use; and as the railways spread
over the land new problems arose for them to face.

The supremacy attained by Great Britain in this period is
largely due to the genius of engineers such as Watt, Telford, the
Stephensons, Brunel and others. In this chapter we shall see the
birth of the first iron bridges and the impact on them of the railway
age. And we shall see how in America the problems were tackled
and solved by men like John A. Roebling, the inventor of the
modern long-span suspension bridge.

*   *   *

Although iron bars were exchanged as currency in England two
thousand years ago and cannon of wrought and cast iron were
used before the reign of Queen Elizabeth, it was not until late in
the eighteenth century that iron was first used for structures as
distinct from machines. By the turn of the century Great Britain
led the iron industry of the world. During this period the first

rolling mill was built by Henry Cort and the first iron bridge in the world, the famous Coalbrookdale bridge over the river Severn, designed by Thomas Farnolls Pritchard and built at the expense of Darby and Wilkinson, two of the early English ironmasters, was completed in 1779. It was an iron arch of 100-foot span carried by a series of semi-circular ribs each of which was cast in two pieces. Only the lowest of the three ribs was continuous right across the span; the upper ribs came to an end beneath the deck, which ran over the top of the arch. They could not therefore take their share in resisting the thrust of the arch, but they did give the bridge greater rigidity. In those early days, as is only to be expected, the designer knew little of the behaviour of metal arches. But it says much for the quality of the iron and the excellence of the workmanship that the bridge remained in service for 170 years and is still carrying traffic to-day.

The first iron bridge in America was not built until some sixty years later; but the next advance was inspired by Tom Paine, famous as the author of *The Rights of Man*. He had designed a cast-iron bridge to span the Schuylkill river; the ribs were cast in Yorkshire, but owing to a financial failure were not shipped to America; instead they were erected in England to form a 236-foot arch bridge over the Wear at Sunderland.

Meanwhile John Rennie senior and Thomas Telford were independently preparing designs for cast-iron arches. Telford was first in the field with the construction of the Buildwas bridge over the Severn. This was designed as a single span, so as to offer least interference with the heavy water-borne traffic of those days and the floods to which the river was subject. Realizing the strength of his material Telford made the arch, like that of the Sunderland ⁻ bridge, much flatter than its forerunner at Coalbrookdale.

*   *   *

In 1800 two problems were troubling the Standing Parliamentary Committee of the Port of London. One of these was the condition of old London bridge, the aged structure which, as we have seen, was little more than a dam, pierced with holes through which the river surged in a torrent at every tide. Not only was it falling to pieces; it formed a barrier that limited the building of docks and wharves to the Pool below the bridge and prevented their extension upstream. There were only two other bridges over the Thames in London at that time, Blackfriars and Westminster; so if London bridge were to be demolished and replaced by a high-level bridge with sufficient headroom for sailing ships to pass beneath it, there would be nothing to stop the extension of the Port of London on either side of the river as far as Black-friars. In August 1800 the Standing Committee reported in favour of this irresistible project. Among the various proposals considered for the new bridge was a characteristically bold design by Telford for a cast-iron arch of 600-foot span. This not only avoided any interference with the waterway but also provided headroom of 65 feet at high water for the masts of ships. To avoid steep gradients for horse-drawn vehicles, long ramped approaches leading up to the bridge were to be built on both shores. Telford was quite confident of his ability to build this bridge. 'If they will only provide the means,' he wrote to a friend, 'and give me elbow room, I see my way as clear as mending the auld brig at the burn.'

For a year or two the matter was actively debated; but on account of the impact of the Napoleonic Wars, and the opposition to the approaches, which would have had to rise high above adjacent buildings, the scheme lapsed. Many years were to pass before an arch of comparable span was built—and then the material used was not cast iron.

Telford turned his mind to his other manifold interests—canals, aqueducts, roads, harbours, and railways; and Londoners had to wait another thirty years before London bridge was replaced by Rennie's multiple arch bridge (subsequently widened) that we know to-day. Probably most people are glad now that the Port of London was not allowed to encroach further west into the City; for if it had, the whole character of central London would have been altered. It is interesting to note on what small circum-stances such far-reaching matters hinge!

* * *

Shortly afterwards, Telford, consulted on the best method of crossing the wide river Mersey at Runcorn, recommended a suspension bridge to be built with iron cables. He had spent the summer of 1814 making tests on the tensile strength of malleable iron and as a result proposed a bridge with a main span 1,000 feet long and two side spans of 500 feet. Telford was also asked to advise on designs submitted by other engineers and thus met Captain Samuel Brown R.N., who, unknown to him, had been working on similar lines. In fact Brown seems to have been the inventor of the wrought-iron link, which he patented in 1817.

Thereafter Telford and Brown exchanged ideas and information, with great benefit, as it turned out, to Telford. For Telford had intended to make the Runcorn bridge with cables built up of a number of square iron bars welded together at the ends. In fact he retained this idea in his first design, prepared shortly afterwards, for a suspension bridge over the Menai Straits (Pl. 8). There were to be sixteen cables each built up of thirty-six iron bars $\frac{1}{2}$ inch square with coped bars on the sides, all bound round with iron wire to form a cable 4 inches in diameter.

Thus it can be seen that Telford, with extraordinary intuition, had visualized something very like the parallel-wire cable used in modern suspension bridges, but with the fatal weakness that, instead of continuous round flexible wire, he proposed to use short stiff iron bars welded together at the ends. It is fortunate for his reputation that the Runcorn bridge project lapsed, because the sag of the cables was to be only 50 feet and on a span of 1,000 feet the cables would have developed nearly their full working stress under their own weight alone. We do not know what made Telford change his views, whether it was that he doubted the strength of the welds, realized the difficulty of construction of such a cable, or that he appreciated the advantages of Brown's type of eyebar chains.

But whatever the cause, he showed his good common sense by adopting wrought-iron links with the reasonable working stress of 5 tons per square inch for the cables of the Menai bridge. The span was 580 feet and there was headroom of 100 feet for shipping. Work began in 1820, and the bridge was completed six years later at a cost of £231,500. It stood for 115 years[1]. The deck was of timber, only 24 feet wide, and carried two lanes of traffic; there was no stiffening truss or any diagonal wind stays. It is not surprising therefore that it was repeatedly damaged by storms. In 1839 the deck was wrecked; part of it fell into the Straits, and the bridgekeeper just had time to row across and stop the London mail coach before it came galloping on to the bridge. A heavier timber deck was built, which survived until 1893, when Sir Benjamin Baker designed and installed a deck of steel. Thereafter the bridge continued in service until it was completely reconstructed in 1940. This work was very skilfully executed; the bridge remained open for traffic throughout the reconstruction and care was taken to interfere as little as possible with its original graceful outline. Some of us may remember Lewis

---

[1] The span of the Menai bridge was surpassed in 1834 by the 870-foot long Fribourg bridge in Switzerland.

Carroll's proposal in *Alice Through the Looking Glass*, 'to keep the Menai bridge from rust by boiling it in wine'. So far as we know engineers have never used good wine for such a purpose! Many of the wrought-iron links of the original bridge were very badly corroded; moreover, they had developed a coarse crystalline structure not at all characteristic of wrought iron and had become brittle with age. The new links were made of high-tensile steel, shot-blasted to remove all scale and rust, then metal-sprayed with a coating of zinc and subsequently given four coats of paint. This is one of the best forms of protection so far devised. At the time of writing, the new links are in perfect condition, far better than that of the other new steelwork which was not given this expensive treatment.

* * *

Another suspension bridge, at Conway, was started soon after and completed in the same year as the Menai bridge. The success of these two caused a wave of enthusiasm for suspension spans. A competition was held for the design of the Clifton bridge over the gorge of the river Avon at Bristol. I. K. Brunel, who was then free from his work on the Thames tunnel, prepared several designs, one of which had the exceptional span of 1,160 feet; but Telford, who was asked to adjudicate, considered that no span longer than that of the Menai bridge could at that time be made safe against wind forces. Brunel thereupon withdrew his designs and in 1830 Telford proposed a suspension bridge of three spans supported on ornamental Gothic towers. When the first enthusiasm evoked by this scheme had died down it was not considered very appropriate and a second competition was held. Brunel entered again, with a design for a 600-foot span, which was accepted. The work on the towers was begun, but abandoned in 1853 on account of the failure of the contractors. Meanwhile Brunel had designed and built the Hungerford bridge, a suspension span to carry foot passengers across the Thames at Charing Cross. Twenty years later the superstructure was removed to make way for the present Charing Cross railway bridge; the brick-faced tower piers of Brunel's bridge were used for the railway bridge and remain to this day. In 1860, a year after the death of Brunel, a new company was formed to complete the Clifton bridge and the cable chains of the Hungerford bridge were re-used at Clifton.

Another well-known engineer, William Tiernay Clark, built three suspension bridges of short span, the Hammersmith bridge, the Norfolk bridge, Shoreham, and the bridge which is still in use over the Thames at Marlow.

His greatest achievement was the old chain bridge over the Danube at Budapest, which took ten years to build and was completed by his brother Adam in 1849 (see p. 153). It had a span 86 feet longer than the Menai bridge and the deck was stiffened by means of heavy railings. This was the first permanent bridge to be built over the Danube below Vienna since the days of Trajan's bridge, seventeen and a half centuries before.

Wrought iron, which was by this time being commercially produced in good quality to satisfy the world-wide demand for Richard Trevithick's high-pressure steam boilers, was rapidly superseding cast iron for structural work. In 1832 the first wrought-iron girder bridge was built near Glasgow; and twenty-one years later, in the Dublin Exhibition, followed the first recorded use of wrought iron lattice girders. The newly improved material was malleable and ductile and much stronger in tension than cast iron; moreover, it could be riveted instead of having to be bolted. This naturally led to the development of the first mechanical riveting machine, designed by Sir William Fairbairn. In 1845 Fairbairn and Robert Stephenson began a series of experiments, the first to be made, on the strength of wrought-iron beams. As a direct result of their knowledge gained in these tests, they embarked on the design for the Britannia and Conway tubular bridges. All the suspension bridges built up to that time had had to carry only horse-drawn roadway traffic; but now, with the advent of the railways, bridges were required to carry very much heavier and more concentrated loads. Moreover, the weakness and lack of rigidity displayed by the early suspension bridges in heavy winds and under repeated rhythmic loads had been most disquieting. A typical case was the Broughton suspension bridge, which failed in 1831 owing to oscillations set up by a body of troops marching in step. A number of suspension bridges built by Sir Samuel Brown, including his well-known Chain Pier bridge at Brighton, had been blown down. His Union bridge over the Tweed at Berwick, which had a span of 449 feet, was completed in 1820 and blown down six months later. The Nassau bridge in Germany was wrecked three years after completion, and the Roche Bernard bridge in France, completed in 1840, with the record span of 641 feet supported by wire cables, had its deck blown off. Two other bridges in America and two in Britain had been shaken down simply by the impact of flocks of sheep or droves of cattle. The first railway suspension bridge built in 1830 by Brown to carry the Stockton and Darlington railway over the Tees had a very brief life. The deck sagged beneath the weight of the trains and rose in a wave in front of them. Within a few years the bridge was literally torn to pieces by the excessive bending.

This long list of failures made Stephenson and Fairbairn realize that the main task before them was to devise a structure with a stiff enough deck; the arrangement and form of the cables were of secondary importance. The bridges were required to carry the Chester and Holyhead railway over the Conway river and the Menai Straits; the latter bridge derived its name from the Britannia Rock in the middle of the crossing (Pl. 6). Stephenson's first proposal was to build two cast-iron arches of 350-foot span, because he realized that an arch was much more rigid and therefore better suited to heavy railway traffic than the suspension type. The arches were ruled out, however, as they could not provide the clear passage 100 feet high throughout the crossing demanded by the Admiralty. Stephenson then evolved the idea of a wrought-iron tube through which the trains would run and which would be supported from cables above it. The recent production of wrought-iron plates and sections for shipbuilding contributed to this design. Stephenson discussed the matter with his father, George, the inventor of the steam locomotive, who thought the idea sound. Small-scale models of tubes of circular, elliptical, and rectangular section were made and tested to destruction at Fairbairn's works; and Eaton Hodgkinson, the mathematician, was called in to assist in interpreting and applying the results to the full-size design.

Stephenson had from the start been somewhat sceptical about the need for chains or cables at all, except for use temporarily to assist in erection, if the tubes were assembled *in situ*. Fairbairn, too, considered them unnecessary, but Hodgkinson wanted to retain them. An alternative method of erection, however, was to float the tubes into position on pontoons and then lift them up bodily into place. When Fairbairn also backed this method it was agreed to adopt it and to dispense finally with any chains or cables. Meanwhile, however, the masonry piers had been built up to the height required for the towers of a suspension bridge. This was now no longer necessary, but the towers were retained; the fine aesthetic appearance of the bridge is therefore to some extent accidental. As to the shape of the tubes, there was serious difference of opinion between Hodgkinson and Fairbairn; probably in order to overcome difficulties in manufacture of circular sections, Stephenson finally decided to have them made rectangular. Before erection, the first tube for the Conway bridge was supported at the ends only and tested by running 300 tons of ballast wagons inside it. This load caused a deflection of only 3 inches and confirmed the accuracy of the design and calculations.

The bridge was opened to traffic in 1850 after Stephenson had himself driven the last one of the 2,000,000 rivets, which is kept white-painted to this day. Both bridges have now survived more than a hundred years, and have never given any cause for anxiety or required more than the normal maintenance, in spite of the ever-increasing weight of traffic. The Britannia bridge has four continuous spans, two of 230 and two of 460 feet, whereas the longest wrought-iron girder previously built had been but 31 feet 6 inches. Such was the magnitude of the advance that Stephenson and Fairbairn made. In effect they designed the first plate girder bridge, the forerunner of the tens of thousands of bridges of this most useful type which can be seen on railways all over the world to-day.

The building of bridges of unprecedented span is always a heavy strain on the engineers responsible. At the opening of the Menai suspension bridge, Telford wanted to cut ceremony to a minimum. To him it was a matter of thanksgiving that the sleepless nights and long days of worry and anxiety were over; his friends who came to congratulate him found him on his knees. Stephenson too, records that 'at night he would lie tossing about seeking sleep in vain. The tubes filled his head. He went to bed and got up with them.' It is only by virtue of the single-minded application to their work of men like these that such masterpieces can be achieved.

*   *   *

What do we know of these men? Telford was born in the valley of Eskdale, Scotland, and was noted for his cheerful disposition which earned him the nickname of 'Laughing Tam'. Always interested in poetry, he later numbered Southey and Campbell amongst his many friends. He had a shrewd sense of humour. Smiles tells how, having patiently listened to a young man's eulogy on an acquaintance of his, Telford quietly asked with a twinkle in his eye, 'Pray, can your friend lay eggs?' By virtue of his intellect he appears to have exercised great influence not only on his fellow engineers but on the Government of the day. Self-reliant, ambitious, public-spirited, masterly, and modest—such are the adjectives that have been applied to him. In 1820 he was elected first President of the Institution of Civil Engineers, and at his death at the age of 77, having built more than 1,200 bridges, he had been for many years the acknowledged head of his profession.

Robert Stephenson inherited not only his father's great wealth, which probably made him the first millionaire-engineer, but also his kindly and upright disposition and cautious approach to the problems he had to tackle. Quietly dressed, prosperous and shrewd, father and son must have presented a marked contrast to the crowd of railway speculators who tried to attract their interest.

Amongst his triumphs Robert Stephenson numbered two famous bridges both still in service to-day, on the east coast route. The High Level bridge at Newcastle comprised six spans of iron arches held by horizontal ties to resist the thrust at the springings. The railway was carried over the top of the arches and the roadway suspended below. The Royal Border bridge at Berwick consisted of twenty-eight semi-circular masonry arches. The foundations were built inside cofferdams, Nasmyth's newly-invented steam hammer being used to drive the piles. Referring to the High Level bridge Samuel Smiles writes:

'The bridge was opened on the 15th August 1849 and, a few days after, the royal train passed over it, halting for a few minutes to enable Her Majesty to survey the wonderful scene below. In the course of the following year the Queen opened the extensive stone viaduct across the Tweed, by which the last link was completed of the continuous line of railway between London and Edinburgh. Over the entrance to the Berwick Station, occupying the site of the once redoubtable Border fortress, so often the deadly battle-ground of the ancient Scots and English, was erected an arch under which the royal train passed, bearing in large letters of gold the appropriate words, " The last act of the Union".'

The advance of the railways had given amazing impetus to bridge-building, so much so that more than 25,000 bridges were built in Great Britain in seventy years.

Whilst Roebling was building his Grand Trunk suspension bridge at Niagara, to which we shall shortly refer, Stephenson wrote to him saying, 'If your bridge succeeds, then mine have been magnificent blunders'. No one, however, bearing in mind its unsurpassed record of service and achievement, would apply this description to the Britannia bridge. Stephenson also designed tubular bridges abroad, including two on the Nile and his great Victoria bridge over the St Lawrence at Montreal. He was by no means infallible, however, when out of his chosen field. Having surveyed the length of the proposed Suez Canal he reported, 'A canal is impossible—it would only be a ditch.'

By his express wish Stephenson was buried near Telford, and the stones marking their resting places lie side by side in the nave of Westminster Abbey.

*　　*　　*

In the New World progress was naturally slower at the start, and it was not until 1842 that any suspension bridge survived longer than a few months. Then Charles Ellett, who had been trained in Paris, built the Fairmount bridge over the Schuylkill River to replace the famous Colossus bridge, which had been destroyed by fire. The new bridge, following the French system, was supported by a number of small wire cables. Ellett next undertook the first bridge over the river below Niagara Falls, to link up the railways in Canada and America. It was a wonderful setting for a bridge; the gorge was 800 feet wide with the foaming waters 200 feet below. Ellett was essentially a showman; he had great self-confidence and was prepared to undertake almost any scheme no matter how impracticable; a few years before he had even advised the mayor of St Louis that a suspension bridge with a span of 6,500 feet was feasible—a rather wild statement to make at a time when no span as much as a tenth of that had been built. Ellett set about the new job in typical fashion. He offered a prize to the first boy to fly a kite across the gorge. By using the kite string to pull a heavier cord, and so on, he strung his first wire rope across. Then, before admiring crowds, Ellett had himself hauled across the gorge and back in an iron basket suspended from the rope—the first man ever to cross Niagara!

A light service bridge only 7½ feet wide was next erected across the gorge, slung on two cables, for the use of the contractor's men on the bridge. Ellett, who for all his showing off was no coward, immediately rode across the narrow swaying platform on horseback. At the time there were not even handrails on the bridge; one false step would have sent horse and rider plunging into the whirlpool below. For ten months a useful profit was made by opening the footbridge to the public on payment of a toll; but then Ellett quarrelled with the promoters of the scheme and his contract was cancelled. He had just completed another span of 1,010 feet over the Ohio river at Wheeling; but its collapse five years later closed his bridge-building career. Adventurous to the last he designed and built a fleet of naval rams. These were used with great success against the enemy's gunboats in the Civil War; but Ellett, recklessly exposing himself to see the effect of their onslaught, was shot.

The work of completing the bridge across Niagara, begun by Ellett, was entrusted to John A. Roebling, an immigrant from Germany. Roebling was a tall man of commanding presence. His deep-set eyes were overhung by shaggy eyebrows beneath a high wide forehead. He had an iron will, immense powers of concentration and spoke rarely but then without reserve. Life had been hard and, perhaps because of his Teutonic outlook, we seem to see Roebling striving in a blood-red Wagnerian sunset—triumphing, to be sure, but at what a cost!—until the tragic end. He became interested in wire ropes for use instead of hemp ropes for hauling heavy boats and their cargoes up the inclines on canal portages. In 1841 he made his first twisted, or stranded, wire ropes and then conceived the idea of making bridge cables of numbers of parallel wires uniformly tensioned and formed into a compact bunch with binding wire. He applied for a patent in March 1841; and thus was born the system, direct, straightforward, and simple, like most great inventions, which is used for making the cables of nearly all American suspension bridges to-day.

Roebling had already built a number of suspended aqueducts and bridges and had set up his new works for the manufacture of wire rope at Trenton. His reputation was established and he eagerly set about the design and construction of the Grand Trunk bridge at Niagara. It was to have two decks, the upper one to carry a single-track railway and the lower one for roadway traffic. The span was to be 820 feet between the centres of the masonry towers. There were to be four main cables 10 inches in diameter built up of parallel wrought-iron wires. Stiffening trusses 18 feet deep were to be constructed between the upper and lower decks. Not only were inclined stays, so much favoured by Roebling, to be used to stiffen the bridge above the deck, but more diagonal cables were fixed later below the roadway and anchored to the sides of the gorge to help the bridge to resist uplift forces due to wind beneath the deck.

In March 1855, after four years of gruelling work, and in spite of an epidemic of cholera that threatened to bring the job to a standstill, the bridge was completed. Thus Roebling's faith in his ability to build a suspension bridge to carry railway traffic was vindicated. Roebling proudly reported: 'With an engine of 28 tons we pushed over from Canada to New York twenty double-loaded freight cars making a gross weight of 368 tons; this train very nearly covered the whole length of floor between the towers . . . . No vibrations whatever.' In his report to the Directors, Roebling stated: 'Bridges of half a mile span, for common or railway travel, may be built, using iron for the cables, with entire safety. But by substituting the best quality of steel wire, we may nearly double the span and afford the same degree of security.' This was a bold and true prophecy; but let us look at the performance of the Niagara bridge. After twenty-six years the wooden suspended structure was replaced by iron and steel; after another four years iron towers were substituted for the original masonry ones, and then in 1897, after forty-two years of service and continual repairs necessitated by failures in the stiffening truss, the bridge was dismantled, to be replaced by a new one capable of carrying the increased weight of traffic. But the new bridge, designed by L. L. Buck, was an arch—a rigid steel bridge of 550 foot span, much more suited than a suspension bridge to such a site and to the concentrated loading of railway traffic.

The record of the other suspension bridges over the Niagara is not a happy story. In 1850 Serrell built a light bridge of 1,043 foot span over the river at Lewiston. No adequate stiffening was provided; the bridge suffered severely in a gale, and Roebling, who happened to be in the district, supplied a number of wire rope cables to anchor the deck to the sides of the gorge to prevent the bridge from being lifted by the wind. A few years later these ropes were temporarily undone, as a heavy ice jam in the river had piled up and threatened to carry them away. When the ice had gone, but before the guys had been re-fixed, a gale sprang up and the bridge fell an easy prey.

It was not until 1867 that a charter was granted to build the first Niagara-Clifton bridge below the Falls. The work was entrusted to Samuel Keefer, and two years later the bridge was completed; it had a wooden deck only 10 feet wide and the record span of 1,268 feet. It was immediately a success; carriages queued to drive across so that their occupants could enjoy the wonderful close-up view of the waterfall, see the grinding pack ice in the winter, and the foaming torrent and whirlpool below. After a year or two the deck was re-built and the wooden stiffening chords and towers replaced by steel; then in 1888 the bridge was widened and virtually reconstructed in steel by

McNulty. Seven months later in a terrific gale it was totally destroyed. One of the last men to cross the span at midnight said that it was rocking 'like a boat in a heavy sea' and that the deck was tipping up 'almost on its very edge'. The bridge was replaced within the year, but was taken down eight years later as it was found not stiff enough to carry the new electric trolley cars that had come into use.

So ended the last of the suspension bridges over Niagara. A few years later this bridge was replaced by the Niagara-Clifton arch which became known as the 'Honeymoon bridge'. Perhaps the most curious point about the Niagara story is that not until forty-five years after the first attempts were made did any engineer see the problem as a whole and derive the right solution.

Chapter 7

THE SHAPES ARISE!

The shapes arise!
Shapes of factories, arsenals, foundries, markets,
Shapes of the two-threaded tracks of railroads,
Shapes of the sleepers of bridges, vast frameworks, girders,
arches. . .

WALT WHITMAN

IN THE second half of the nineteenth century iron gave way to
steel for use in the superstructure of bridges, and methods of
sinking foundations below water by means of compressed air were
steadily developed and improved. Some famous bridges were
built, including Brunel's Saltash bridge and the St Louis bridge
over the Mississippi river, which was the first big bridge of
steel arches and was erected by the modern cantilever method.
Then, with a numbing shock, came the tragedy of the Tay bridge.
This disaster shook the confidence of engineers and awakened
them to an appreciation of what wind forces could do, even to
heavy rigid girders. There followed the triumphant opening of
the Brooklyn bridge in America, the first long-span bridge to be
built of steel. This masterpiece of John Roebling and his son
pointed the way for all the great suspension bridges in America
to-day.

Like most important innovations, the use of steel was slow to
become established. In fact three years after Bessemer's process
of steel conversion was announced in 1866 the Board of Trade
banned Sir John Hawkshaw from using steel in the Charing Cross
railway bridge. This prohibition was still in effect when the
Siemens open-hearth method of steel production was established;
and it was not until 1877, just before the construction of the Forth
bridge, that the ban was removed.

The most famous of the early wrought-iron spans to follow the
Britannia bridge was the Saltash or Royal Albert bridge built by
I. K. Brunel in 1855-59 (Pl. 7). This was Brunel's last and greatest

bridge, and although the massive wrought-iron tubes that form its curved upper chord look strange to us to-day, it showed a marked advance in appearance, and of course in magnitude, on his earlier Chepstow bridge. It is also noteworthy that Brunel, who had gained valuable experience of compressed air work in the Thames tunnel, adopted this method for sinking the main foundation in mid-stream. Compressed air was first used on bridge foundations in 1851 by Cubitt and John Wright for sinking the cylinder piers for the bridge at Rochester on the Medway to a depth of 61 feet. Brunel had used the process on a small scale at Chepstow, but Saltash was the first big bridge for which it was employed. Subsequently, the method came into general use, and this may be a convenient point to give a description of it.

* * *

We have seen in Chapter 1 how bridge piers were built inside cofferdams, which were in effect enclosures made of sheet piling driven in the river bed. When the cofferdam, which was open top and bottom, was pumped out, the subsoil could be excavated inside it and the pier built in the dry. But this method had two serious limitations: it could not be used when the river bed was of rock as the piles could not be driven; and it could not be used for deep foundations as the piles were too short, nor were they strong enough to resist the pressure from a great depth of water or subsoil.

It was to overcome these difficulties that caissons were invented. A caisson differs from a cofferdam in that it has a working chamber at the bottom of it which is enclosed on top and from which the water is excluded by means of compressed air (Fig. 17). The essential parts of a compressed air caisson are: a box, or working chamber, with open bottom, which is lowered onto the river bed and in which men excavate the subsoil; an access shaft, leading from the working chamber up to the surface for the passage of men and materials; an air lock, at the top of the access shaft, which comprises a man lock and a muck lock to enable men and materials, respectively, to pass into the caisson from the atmospheric pressure outside to the compressed air within, and vice versa; and the air compressors to provide and maintain the requisite pressure in the working chamber. As the depth increases, so the water pressure increases, and the air pressure has to be raised to balance it. At a depth of 120 feet, the pressure is 52 lb. per square inch; this is the greatest pressure in which men can work, even in very short shifts, without considerable risk and discomfort. .

Unless proper precautions are taken, men coming out of compressed air suffer caisson disease, or 'bends', so-called on account of the terrible cramping pains which double a man up when he is afflicted by them. The severity of the disease may vary from earache and nose-bleeding to permanent paralysis and death. As we shall see, in the early days of compressed air work, neither the cause of the disease nor the means of avoiding it were understood; no cure was available and many fatalities resulted. In 1876, however, the French physiologist Paul Bert discovered that the disease was caused by bubbles of nitrogen becoming liberated in the blood and tissues during decompression, thus partially arresting the circulation; and that it could be avoided by working shorter shifts and also by decompressing very slowly, particularly from high pressure.

Further investigation was made at the beginning of this century by Dr. Leonard Hill and his colleague Greenwood, who repeatedly undertook experiments on themselves in compressed air at pressures up to 75 lb. per square inch. In fact on one occasion Greenwood raised the pressure as high as 92 lb. They found that tissues of fat formed an extraordinary depository for excess of nitrogen; tests on animals showed that the less the weight of the body, the more quickly could it be saturated by nitrogen and thereafter drained of it. Hence the conclusion, borne out by experience, that young, small, wiry men are best suited to high-pressure work. Dr. Hill explained that the symptoms of caisson disease depended on where the bubbles of nitrogen were liberated. 'If in the joints they caused pain in the joints, in the muscles they caused pain in the muscles, in the nervous system they caused paralysis, in the heart they caused sudden death.'

To-day, after working four hours at a pressure of 40 lb. per square inch, not less than 105 minutes would be required for decompression. A recent development has been that of 'stage decompression', in which men are brought out from the highest pressures to atmosphere in ten minutes or so; they are at once put under pressure again in a large recompression chamber and are subsequently decompressed slowly. This system has many advantages. It enables the air locks to be freed quickly; moreover, the big recompression chamber can be properly heated and ventilated and there is space for men to take exercise, to sit in comfort, or, for suspected cases of bends, to lie down. They can have hot drinks to stimulate the circulation, be given any necessary medical attention, read or play cards. Recompression in a 'medical lock', as it is called, and subsequent slow decompression is now known to be the proper treatment for bends.

The sensations as the pressure rises in the air lock are very peculiar. Voices sound cracked and thin; sense of touch becomes less acute and sense of smell disappears altogether. To work in compressed air, men have to be fit; monthly medical inspections

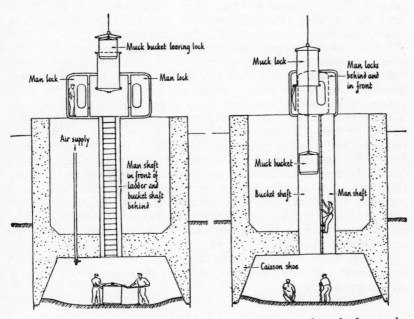

FIG. 17. Diagrammatic sections of a compressed air caisson, from the front and the side. For clarity the air inlets and fittings on the locks are omitted.

are the rule, and no man suffering from a cold in the head or sore throat is admitted. Alcohol is barred.

So long as the cutting edge at the bottom of the caisson is in water, the working chamber will be 'sealed' and the compressed air inside cannot escape. But it is quicker and more efficient to work in the dry and the tendency therefore is to raise the air pressure slightly above that required to balance the hydrostatic head and so expel all water from the caisson. If the air pressure rises too high, however, and the air finds a weak spot in the ground, it may suddenly break out and a lot escape. This is known as a 'blow'; it is by no means a common occurrence but may occur in soft or variable ground unless the air pressure is carefully regulated. Owing to the air blowing out, the pressure inside the caisson falls quickly, with the result that moisture condenses out of the air, forming a sudden thick fog. At the same time air rushes down the shaft to replace that which has escaped, setting up a roar like a huge organ pipe. Then, as the pressure inside the caisson has fallen, water begins to flow back into the working chamber and will rise until the air pressure inside once again balances the hydrostatic head.

'Blows' usually appear more alarming than they are, but they can be serious and there have even been instances of men blown out of the working chamber under the cutting edge. The most terrible tragedy on record occurred during the sinking of a caisson in the bed of the river Neva at St Petersburg in 1876-78. The caisson, which was in very soft ground, suddenly plunged down 59 feet. Of twenty-eight men in the working chamber nineteen had time to escape up the shaft as the mud and water flowed in, but nine were imprisoned. It was twenty-eight hours before the rescue parties succeeded in reaching them and by that time only two remained alive. A year passed before work was renewed and then there was another disaster. Under the high pressure one of the locks gave way. Nine men were blown bodily up the shaft out of the caisson and killed; twenty others were smothered by the inrushing mud and water in the working chamber. Now that engineers have had many years experience of compressed air work, however, there is little possibility of such an occurrence to-day.

* * *

The Saltash bridge was required to carry a single track of what was then the Cornwall railway. At the selected crossing the river Tamar was 1,100 feet wide with a depth at high water of 70 feet. Brunel decided to build two spans of 455 feet, requiring one large pier in mid-stream, and a number of short, curved approach spans. Borings showed that there was a foundation of hard greenstone traprock[1] available, 16 feet below the mud, for the middle pier, but that the rock had a rough and sloping surface. Brunel designed a cylinder of wrought iron 35 feet in diameter, the bottom being formed to an inclination of 1 in 6 to conform

[1] Dark-coloured eruptive rock of columnar structure.

to the slope of the rock. The cylinder was built on shore, floated off on the tide, towed to site, and sunk in the correct position. By means of compressed air, the water was expelled from the working chamber, the mud was excavated by hand, the rock dressed, and the caisson securely founded. An air pressure of 35 lb. per square inch was needed to keep the water out at the depth of 80 feet. The seven-hour shifts that were first worked proved far too long and when they came out the men suffered from temporary paralysis. The shifts were reduced to three hours and then, although some forty men were employed in the working chamber, there was no more illness.

The superstructure represents a combination of arch and suspension bridge. The upper chord, which acts as an arch in compression, consists of a huge wrought-iron cylinder, oval in section; the lower chord is formed of two suspension chains in tension, anchored to the ends of the arch. The rise of the arch-shaped tubes is the same as the sag of the chains, the depth between the two at mid-span being 56 feet. The tube and chains are braced together by means of diagonal ties and vertical struts, from which the deck is suspended. In this design we can see the first glimmerings of the modern bridge truss, consisting of upper and lower chords with diagonal bracing between them. Robert Stephenson was heading the same way in his High Level bridge at Newcastle, which was the first tied arch or 'bowstring girder'. The earliest iron truss bridges were evolved from the plate girders which came into use all over Great Britain in the railway age. As spans and depth increased, the solid web plate was replaced by a latticework of flat bars, which in time gave way to systems of diagonal bracing. Thus was born the triangulated truss bridge which is universally used, although unfortunately sufficient thought is not always given to its appearance.

Brunel had been present as an onlooker during the critical stages of erection of the Conway and Britannia bridges and adopted a very similar method at Saltash. The two main spans, each of which weighed 1,060 tons, were built on shore and floated out on pairs of pontoons. When the span was exactly positioned on the piers, the pontoons were partially flooded and towed out as the tide fell. The span then had to be lifted bodily through a height of 100 feet to its final level. This was done by means of hydraulic jacks at each end, the masonry of the piers being built up beneath the truss after each 3 foot lift (Pl.7). Unfortunately, Brunel could only attend one of the lifting operations as he was busy preparing for the launch of his famous steamship the *Great Eastern*. The bridge was completed at a cost of £225,000 and opened by the Prince Consort in May 1859.

Brunel, who had been appointed engineer of the newly-projected Great Western railway at the age of 27, was boldly unconventional in his ideas. He never played safe, but his projects were generally successful. It was he who persuaded the Railway Company to build the first steamship, the *Great Western*, to make regular voyages across the Atlantic from Bristol to New York. Subsequently he was a keen protagonist of the Great Exhibition of 1851. In all his work on bridges, tunnels, ships, and railways, he never spared himself, but, smoking his inevitable cigars, worked up to all hours of the night. The year before he was due to follow his friend Robert Stephenson as President of the Institution of Civil Engineers, Brunel died. His bridge still stands, and has been carrying main-line traffic for more than ninety years. The approach spans were renewed in 1928-29, but the two main spans are exactly the same, except for maintenance, as when they were originally built.

*   *   *

The next step forward was the St Louis bridge over the mighty Mississippi (Pl. 9). The river is 1,500 feet wide with a sandy bed overlying rock, the depth of which varies from 54 feet to 136 feet below high water. Every summer the turbid, swiftly flowing stream rises 40 feet, scouring out the sand down to bedrock; in the winter it may be blocked for weeks by an ice barrier up to 20 feet thick. From 1839 onwards designs for a bridge had been prepared by Ellett, Roebling, and Homer, the last-named proposing three tubular spans of 500 feet, on the lines of the Britannia bridge. Finally, in 1867, James B. Eads was appointed engineer and his design for a bridge of three arches, with centre span of 520 feet and two side spans of 502 feet, was accepted. The arch-type was preferred to suspension as the bridge had to sustain railway loading. It was made double-decked to carry roadway traffic on the upper deck and two railway tracks below.

Eads was a most efficient, painstaking, and competent engineer. He paid two visits to Europe, in the course of which he discussed problems of the quality of the steel to be used and the method of sinking the foundations. He found Brereton, Brunel's assistant on the Saltash bridge, most helpful. He met Moreaux, the eminent French engineer, who had built more than a thousand bridges and who at first thought it presumptuous that an American should attempt to built steel arches of 200 feet greater span than the longest in Europe; but when he had examined the plans, Moreaux described them as thorough and complete and showing engineering ability of the highest order.

Eads rightly decided that the foundations must be carried down to rock, although this necessitated the use of compressed air to a depth at which it had never been employed before. Since Brunel's work at Saltash, the pneumatic method had been improved by Fleur Saint Denis in the foundations of the bridge over the Rhine at Kehl. He had used rectangular iron caissons, entered by air shafts in the modern manner, with the locks at the top. It was no doubt on grounds of economy that, although iron caissons had been used on these bridges, Eads reverted to the use of timber sheathed with iron for the biggest caisson at St Louis, and Roebling used timber caissons at Brooklyn. Although timber may remain remarkably well preserved when buried out of reach of air, it is not as durable a material, or as suitable for the foundation of a great bridge as iron or concrete.

The caissons for the two channel piers of the Eads bridge were built with a double skin of iron plate, stiffened inside by cast-iron frames and timber struts. Although one of the piers was isolated by heavy ice floes for fifteen days, sinking proceeded steadily until both piers were founded on the rock. The biggest and deepest caisson, however, was that for the east abutment. It was six-sided and measured 82 feet by 72 feet overall; it was made of timber, sheathed outside in iron plating $\frac{3}{8}$ inch thick. When the cutting edge was still 10 feet from the rock the work was delayed by a tornado of terrific violence. Cranes were blown down, ships wrecked, and scaffolding smashed. The force of the wind was such that a locomotive weighing 25 tons was lifted clean off the railway embankment and landed upside down at the bottom. Eads at once strengthened his design, incorporating iron wind-bracing beneath the deck of the bridge from end to end.

The caisson was sunk to rock comparatively uneventfully, except for the effect of the high air pressure on the sinkers. After working at a depth of just over 100 feet, one of the men collapsed and died fifteen minutes after leaving the air-lock; this was ascribed to apoplexy, but within a few days, in spite of energetic medical supervision, several more deaths occurred. How little the cause of caisson disease was understood is illustrated by the fact that the sinkers were issued with bands of armour to be worn around the wrists, ankles, arms, waist, and also under the soles of the feet! These 'safeguards', which were intended to assist by means of galvanic action, were made of alternate scales of zinc and silver. We know now that the reason for the fatalities was that the men were taking only two or three minutes to decompress from 40 lb. per square inch. In the final stages of the deep east abutment, the working shifts were reduced to half an hour each; but it was not realized at that time that slow decompression was just as important as not working too long under pressure. Out of 600 men employed on sinking, there were 119 serious cases of 'bends' and 14 men died; the majority of the fatalities were men who had only worked one or two shifts. It was many years before another bridge foundation was sunk to such a depth.

After the rock had been dressed, the caissons were plugged with concrete, the working chambers filled with sand, and the masonry piers constructed. Each span consisted of four ribs side by side, each rib being composed of two parallel arched tubes, one twelve feet above the other, interconnected by diagonal bracing. The tubes were made of $\frac{1}{4}$-inch steel plate, bent to a diameter of 18 inches, riveted at the seams, and lined inside with specially-shaped steel staves. Wrought-iron bands were shrunk onto the ends of each tube; the connections were then faced and threaded so that they could be screwed together by means of sleeve couplings. It was found that to roll staves that were not too soft, chrome steel had to be used; and it is an extraordinary thing that this quality of steel, which is very similar in properties to some of the high-tensile steel recently developed for bridgework, was obtainable eighty years ago.

During erection the ribs of the arches were tied back by cables passing over the tops of temporary towers built on the piers. The work, which was slow and exacting, was under the direct charge of Theodore Cooper, a young engineer whom we shall meet again. The arches had to be kept true to line and level, allowances being made for the effect of changes of temperature, the stretch of the cables, and the compression of the tubes. But there were many other difficulties and dangers. On one occasion Cooper tripped on a plank and fell 90 feet to the river. He had the presence of mind to curl up, so far as he could, before he hit the water, and was uninjured; a boat soon picked him up and after a change of clothing he returned to work. Another embarrassment was that a loan of half a million dollars, which Eads had negotiated in London, depended on the closing of the first arch by 19 September 1873. But when this operation was attempted on 15 September, the gap for the last tube was found to be slightly too small, so that the piece would not go in. Calculations showed that if the temperature of the erected steelwork could be reduced to 44°F. it would contract sufficiently to widen the gap and admit the tube. So it was decided to pack the span with ice. The chords of the bridge were wrapped in gunny cloths and 15 tons of ice packed round them in wooden troughs. The work continued day and night and the space wanted was reduced from $2\frac{1}{4}$ inches to $\frac{5}{8}$ inch. Forty-five more tons of ice were used in an attempt to open the gap the last $\frac{5}{8}$ inch, but it was of no avail; in spite of every effort the distance could not be increased. On the 17th it was decided to use slightly shorter tubes adjustable in length, which had been prepared for the emergency, and by nightfall they were safely inserted; thus was the arch closed, although not with the exactitude that had been intended, and the loan secured. Cooper and his men had been constantly at work for sixty-five hours and were nearly exhausted. He said, 'We were so sleepy that it was almost impossible to keep our eyes open, and I was afraid some of us would go into the river. Many of the men had left and only about half a dozen remained to the last.'

After the arches were closed the erection of the deck and roadway proceeded quickly, and in July the bridge was tested by means of fourteen locomotives weighing 700 tons. It was then opened to traffic and is still in use to-day. It was the first of the big arch bridges made of iron and steel, and the cantilever method of erection adopted has been followed, with only one notable exception (see page 149) for all its successors. It is also of interest that steel was used in this bridge in America several years before its use was permitted in England.

* * *

On 1 June 1878 the fine new two-mile long Tay bridge was opened to carry main-line railway traffic between Edinburgh and Dundee. It was a single-track bridge, and over the navigable waterway were thirteen tall narrow spans standing high above the river. Most of these girders were 245 feet long and consisted of wrought-iron trusses standing on cast-iron columns rising from piers of brick and concrete. Designed by Sir Thomas Bouch and built at a cost of £350,000, the bridge was heralded as the latest and greatest engineering masterpiece; but a few months after it was opened, it was found that the wrought-iron cross-bracing between some of the piers had worked loose, probably due to the strains produced by storms of wind. At that time there was no Standard Specification, based on sound knowledge, stating the wind pressures to be assumed in the design of bridges. The pressures generally adopted were taken from the table presented by Smeaton to the Royal Society in 1759—more than a hundred years before:—

> 6 lb. per square foot for 'high winds'
> 8 or 9 lb. per square foot for 'very high winds'
> 12 lb. per square foot for a 'storm or tempest'

It is not clear what wind pressure was actually adopted in the design of the Tay bridge. There is some suggestion that a pressure of 20 lb. per square foot was used, but Sir Thomas Bouch subsequently stated that no special provision for wind pressure had been made. Nor was any continuous lateral wind-bracing provided below the deck.

On Sunday afternoon, 28 December 1879, a storm sprang up. As evening drew on, the wind was blowing such a gale that some of the citizens of Dundee, their hearts filled with foreboding for the new bridge, went out to the north signal box to watch for the arrival of the Edinburgh Mail. At a quarter past seven, when the storm was at the height of its fury, the train driver took his bâton from the signalman and the train moved slowly out onto the bridge. A few minutes later the watchers saw a flash of sparks in the darkness and then a long comet of light sweeping down to the waters of the Tay. The signalman tried to get into touch by telegraph with his mate at the other end of the bridge but found that something was wrong with the line. Then two men, at the risk of their lives in such a gale, crawled along the track until they came to a point where the bridge in front of them had disappeared. The thirteen high spans, more than half a mile of the bridge, with the train on it, had been blown down. There were no survivors and it is estimated that seventy-five persons lost their lives.

At the official enquiry it transpired that a wind force of about 40 lb. per square foot would have been required to overturn the bridge and its columns; this would correspond to a wind velocity of about 115 m.p.h. and it seems most unlikely that the storm could have reached such an intensity over such a big area. The cause of the disaster will never be known, but it may well be that the explanation put forward by Gröthe, the resident engineer during construction, is the most probable. The part of the bridge that fell consisted of three groups of continuous spans, with expansion joints over the piers between them. Owing to the continuity of the girders, when the train was on the span next-but-one to an expansion joint, there would be a tendency for the end of the girder at the expansion joint to lift off its bearings, somewhat like one end of a seesaw. Gröthe thought that this must have happened, and that the end of the span had been blown off its bearings and had come down, smashing the columns below it. The position of the train, which was found in the span next but one to an expansion joint bears out this theory. If the spans had not been made continuous there would have been no tendency for the end of this girder to lift and the disaster might not have occurred.

The details of the expansion bearings support this theory. No tie down of any kind was provided; moreover, as the sides of the rollers and bearing plate were sloping instead of vertical, they would readily permit the end of the girder, if it lifted, to be blown off sideways. If this had happened at any one of the expansion bearings on the high spans, the girders in falling would have brought down the piers at both ends and all thirteen spans would undoubtedly have crashed.

Sir Thomas Bouch was so shocked by the disaster that his health broke down and he died a year later. In 1882-87 the bridge was rebuilt to carry two tracks on a site close alongside the old one. Much of the ironwork of the old bridge was re-used and a wind force of 56 lb. per square foot was allowed for in the design of the new bridge. It was perhaps only natural that after such a calamity the new requirements for wind pressure laid down by the Board of Trade should err on the side of safety; in the British Standard Specification of to-day the pressure has been reduced to 30 lb. per square foot. The second bridge, which was built by Messrs William Arrol & Co., is still standing, and is one of the longest bridges over water in the world.

The Tay bridge disaster is the best-known example of the failure of a bridge by lack of aerostatic stability. Its failure was of an entirely different type from that of the early suspension bridges which, as we have seen, were blown down because they lacked aerodynamic rigidity. In the latter case, the force of the wind set up progressively increasing oscillations of the bridge; the whole structure became alive, with the deck undulating and rocking and twisting until the bridge literally tore itself to pieces. But the Tay bridge behaved in no such manner; up to the moment of disaster, when the spans were bodily displaced by the wind, they showed no signs of movement. Another dramatic failure similar to that of the Tay bridge occurred when the Chester bridge over the Mississippi river was blown down in 1944. This was a cantilever bridge in which the spans were very narrow for their height, and were blown off the piers into the river.

Before the Tay bridge fell, Sir Thomas Bouch had prepared

designs for a suspension bridge over the Firth of Forth. It was to have two spans of 1,600 feet and work had actually commenced at Inchgarvie. As he was uncertain what wind pressure to adopt on such a span, the designer had consulted four other eminent engineers and also the Astronomer Royal, who gave it as their reasoned opinion that provision for a pressure of 10 lb. per square foot would be ample. This advice, however, does not appear to have been based on any adequate tests or measurements, and illustrates the degree of ignorance that prevailed. After the disaster at the Tay, Sir Thomas Bouch's engagement to design the Forth bridge was cancelled, and subsequently Sir John Fowler and Benjamin Baker were appointed in his place. They carried out a series of experiments, measuring the force of wind of various velocities on large vertical areas. Ultimately a wind pressure of 56 lb. per square foot, as specified by the Board of Trade and shown to be ample by the series of wind tests, was adopted. This was five and a half times the pressure that had previously been contemplated and thus it appears that the fall of the Tay bridge may have averted an even greater disaster at the Forth. Although the wind pressure used for the Forth bridge was excessive it gave the bridge a margin of strength which made it well able to bear the increasing weight of railway traffic it was later called on to carry.

*   *   *

In May 1867, John Roebling was appointed chief engineer for the design and construction of the Brooklyn bridge across the East river, to link Long Island with New York. The span was to be 1,595½ feet, nearly half as long again as the longest so far built; and the bridge had to carry two street car, and two elevated line tracks, two lanes of roadway traffic, and a footway. While Roebling prepared the design and calculations, his son made a tour of Europe, studying the latest developments in the manufacture of structural steel and wire, and the pneumatic method of caisson sinking. Then, a year after his return, the first of the misfortunes that were to beset the work fell upon them. As John Roebling was engaged on a survey to fix the position of the Brooklyn pier, his foot was crushed by a ferry boat. Amputation of the toes was necessary, lockjaw set in, and in July 1869 Roebling died. Such a disaster might well have caused the abandonment of the bridge. But Roebling had left a trained and devoted disciple in his son. On his deathbed he handed over the fulfilment of the task he had undertaken, and next month Washington Roebling was appointed his successor. And what a legacy it proved to be! Thirteen years of ceaseless struggle against prejudice, ignorance, officialdom, financial difficulties, labour troubles, and, last but not least the forces of nature herself. At the start the bridge took the life of its designer, and before it was finished had devoured the health and strength of the man who saw it through to completion.

The Brooklyn caisson had to be sunk 44 feet below high water in order to reach a secure foundation; but the caisson on the New York side had to penetrate to a depth of 78 feet. The caissons were made of timber, the walls being 9 feet thick at the top and tapering to the base, where they were built onto heavy cast-iron cutting edges. The roofs were also of timber, 15 feet thick ultimately in the Brooklyn caisson and 22 feet thick on the New York side. The caissons were constructed on slipways beside the river, launched broadside-on, and floated into position. Masonry was built on top of the caisson until it had sufficient weight to sink into the river bed, which had been levelled off to receive it. Compressed air was then applied and excavation began.

The caisson differed from modern ones in many ways, one of which was the incorporation of vertical dredging shafts open at the top and bottom. The compressed air was prevented from escaping by keeping the bottom of these shafts always immersed in water (Pl. 10). In the Brooklyn caisson a most spectacular 'blow' of a unique kind occurred early one Sunday morning, but fortunately at a time when there was no one in the working chamber. The water seal at the bottom of one of the dredging shafts was accidentally allowed to fall below the level of the bottom of the shaft; immediately with a deafening roar the whole of the compressed air in the caisson escaped up the shaft. A huge column of water, mud and fog shot hundreds of feet up into the air. Bereft of its air pressure the caisson settled 10 inches into the river bed; but it was undamaged and after the water seal had been made good and the locks closed the air pressure was quickly restored.

A much more serious occurrence was the fire that broke out in one of the oakum seams of the timber roof of the caisson—probably due to the necessity for using candles and other naked lights, as electric lamps had not then been invented. The effect of the air pressure was to drive the fire deep into the timber roof and out of sight. Before it could be put out, the whole caisson had to be flooded. It was subsequently found that the fire had destroyed a large part of the third and fourth courses of timber in the roof;

all the charred wood had to be cut out and made good with new timber and concrete, as a consequence of which the job was delayed more than two months. Profiting by this experience, Roebling had the inside of the New York caisson lined with thin sheet iron.

It was in the New York foundation, however, where the air

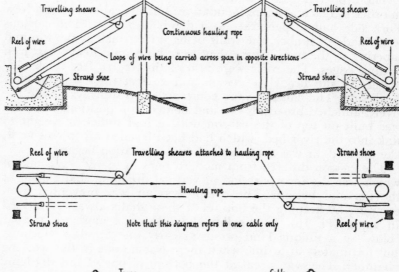

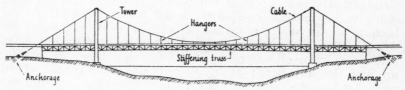

FIG. 18. An elevation of a modern suspension bridge with two sketches above showing, diagrammatically, the method of spinning the cables.

pressure amounted to 36 lb. per square inch, that the worst trouble from caisson disease developed. Altogether there were more than a hundred serious cases, the most tragic of them being that of Roebling himself. At the time of the fire he had spent many hours under compressed air, directing the fire fighters, and was at one time carried out unconscious, only to return again as soon as he had recovered. Always in the lead, he had probably spent more hours under compressed air than any man on the job. At last the strain of his labours proved too great; worn out with toil and worry Roebling succumbed and remained crippled and partially paralysed for the rest of his life.

But year by year the building of the bridge went on. The foundations were sealed with concrete and the Gothic masonry towers built up to their commanding height. The anchorages for the cables were constructed; the first catwalk was slung across the span; and then the long task of spinning the cables over the top of the towers, from the Brooklyn to the New York anchorage was begun. At the last moment Roebling decided that the bridge cables must be made of galvanized cast steel wire.

The method of spinning cables is essentially simple (Fig. 18). From the reel of wire at one end of the bridge a loop is carried over the span by means of a spinning wheel attached to a hauling rope. When the loop of wire reaches the far anchorage, it is pulled off the spinning wheel by hand and placed round a 'strand shoe' which connects it to the anchorage. At the near end the wire is also placed round a strand shoe of the near anchorage. Another loop is then carried across on the wheel and so the spinning proceeds. Each wire is checked for level, at the centre of the span and in the side spans, against a guide wire, to ensure that all wires have the same sag. All the wires in one strand are connected to the same shoe, sufficient shoes being provided at each anchorage for all the strands in the cable.

So the spinning proceeded, until all the wires were laid and each strand connected round the shoes at the anchorages. Then the wires of the cables were squeezed together (Pl. 11); the cable bands and hangers placed, and the steelwork of the deck and stiffening trusses erected. Finally in May 1883, amidst scenes of memorable excitement the bridge was opened. Since then it has carried a huge volume of traffic for some seventy years. From time to time the deck has required strengthening, and in 1951 a scheme was put in hand to do away with the tracks and modify the roadway to make it suitable for six lanes of traffic. But the main structure of the bridge remains as a monument to the Roeblings, father and son; to the vision that conceived it and the endurance that brought it to completion.

Chapter 8

BRITISH BRIDGES OVERSEAS

'As for the bridge, so many have died in the building
that it cannot fail.'

RUDYARD KIPLING, *The Day's Work*

'ALL CIVILIZATION begins with a road', and since 1850, roads and
railways built by pioneers from this country have been pushed to
the outposts of an empire[1] many times greater than that of Rome.
British engineers have in fact built many of the biggest bridges
abroad, not only in the empire but also in nearly every other
country. The great majority of these bridges are of steel, but
recently numbers of reinforced concrete spans have been built, and
must be added to the list. Long-span bridges are described later
in the book; this chapter is therefore devoted to a very brief description of a few of the other outstanding bridges built by British
engineers in Europe and overseas.

As we shall see, the greatest activity was in India, where a
characteristic technique of building developed, consisting of
wrought-iron or steel railway bridges, of many spans, carried on
brick wells sunk in the sand. The railways they served proved
invaluable in time of drought and famine, and must have saved
hundreds of thousands of lives.

The opening up of Africa, except for the coastal fringe and the
Nile valley, came at a later date, and a bigger proportion of the
bridges there are for roadway rather than railway traffic.

In Canada the tall lumber forests led to the construction of
timber trestle bridges that were widely used on the railways; but
they proved too vulnerable to fire and have gradually been replaced by steel or concrete. To-day the steel spans of the Dominion
Bridge Co. and other Canadian firms can be seen all over the
country. Canada has recently followed the lead of America, but
with significant modifications, as we shall see, in the construction

---

[1] I have used the term empire throughout because most of the events described
occurred before its metamorphosis into a commonwealth.

of long-span suspension bridges designed and built by Canadian engineers.

In Australia and subsequently in New Zealand the great majority of the early bridges for both railways and highways were built mainly of timber and many are still in use to-day. The first big bridge in Australia was the Hawkesbury River railway bridge built by an American company to link Sydney with New-castle in 1889. Since the completion of Sydney Harbour bridge, Australian engineers have become fully capable of building their own bridges. As an example, the Story bridge at Brisbane, a cantilever with a single span of 924 feet, was designed and built in 1935-40 solely by Australian engineers and labour.

In South America British engineers have built thousands of miles of railway and the bridges on its routes. In Peru the Central Railway runs past the ruins of ancient Inca cities; it skirts the side of moving sandhills, winds past the craters of extinct volcanoes, and pierces the Andes in a tunnel more than 15,000 feet above sea level, near one of the sources of the Amazon. On the Central Argentine railway two of the bridges are more than a mile in length; elsewhere there are single spans more than 600 feet long and many hundreds of shorter ones supplied by British firms.

In Europe there are bridges built by British engineers in almost every country, from Iceland and Finland in the north, to Portugal in the west and Turkey in the east. Amongst the most interesting are the Storstrøm bridge in Denmark and the Vila Franca bridge, consisting of five tied arches of 335-foot span completed in 1951, over the Tagus near Lisbon (Pl. 13).

*　　*　　*

The great Storstrøm bridge over the western part of the tideless Baltic sea is the longest in Europe. It provides a through route for a single track railway and two lanes of roadway traffic over two miles of water between Copenhagen and the Continent. Designed for the Danish State Railways by Messrs Dorman Long & Co., the bridge comprises forty-seven side spans and three long navigation spans. The side spans are plate girders varying from 175 to 204 feet in length; the navigation spans are tied arches, the central one having a span of 447 feet and the two others 336 feet. The foundations, which were built in steel cofferdams, presented no great difficulty, as the greatest depth of water is only 45 feet and the piers are founded in clay.

The method of erection of the superstructure was bold and

novel. The side spans, which weighed up to 500 tons each, were assembled on a slipway on the foreshore and were then hoisted up bodily by means of a huge floating crane and placed on the piers at a height of 90 feet above water level. (Pl. 12). The crane was built specially for the job on two steel, sea-going, dumb barges which had been used for thirty years as grain carriers on the river Elbe. They were purchased in Germany and towed through the Kiel Canal via the open Baltic to the site. Handled by three tugs, the crane could only be used on fairly calm days, as in a wind of more than 20 m.p.h. it would have been uncontrollable.

For the erection of the navigation spans, the biggest of which weighed 1,520 tons (three times the capacity of the floating crane), the method had to be varied. The lower girders, which form the ties of the arches, were erected in two halves by the floating crane and supported on a temporary trestle at the middle. The arch ribs and hangers were then assembled overhead by a travelling crane running on the girders. Comprising no less than 21,000 tons of steel and built at a cost of £1,270,000 the bridge was completed and opened in 1937.

An interesting comparison may be made between the Storstrøm bridge and the existing Tay bridge, built fifty years earlier. What are the main advances in that time? The Storstrøm bridge is built largely of high-tensile steel, and plate girders and tied arches have been preferred to lattice girders of the kind used over the Tay. These changes give improved economy and appearance. Moreover, the whole of the Storstrøm bridge steelwork was cleaned of rust and mill scale[1] by means of sand blasting, instead of the old system of scraping and wire brushing. In addition permanent painting travellers and gangways are provided to give access to all parts. This, together with the use of plate girders, which are easier to clean and paint than lattice trusses, shows the modern emphasis on maintenance.

During the first year an average of 1,000 vehicles per day made the crossing. This was about four times the number that had used the car ferry and shows how a well-sited bridge attracts traffic and thereby stimulates trade.

A further point of interest in this bridge was the failure of some of the steel hangers of the navigation spans. These hangers were built up of single web plates with four angles, making an I-section; during construction of the bridge, the outstanding legs of some of the angles were found to be fractured at the top. Investigation failed to reveal any weakness in the material, and the fractures

[1] Hard blue scale on the surface of rolled steel.

were ascribed to fatigue under prolonged vibration principally caused by wind. It was found that there was close agreement between the natural period of vibration of the longest hangers and that of the complete span. Considerable vibration due to wind had, moreover, been observed and two of the failures were found following a severe gale. The difficulty was overcome by substituting hangers of stiffer section to obviate the vibration.

* * *

Typical examples of the outstanding achievements of Australian engineers are the two fine bridges recently completed for road and railway traffic (Pl. 14) over the Hawkesbury river some thirty miles from Sydney. These were designed respectively by the Department of Main Roads and the Department of Railways of New South Wales. The description below is confined to the road bridge, on which the greater difficulties were encountered.

At the south end of the bridge there are two welded steel spans 440 feet long with riveted connections. Owing to the steeply shelving rock, overlaid for a depth of nearly 200 feet by beds of silt, clay, and sand, the task of building the pier between these two spans proved very formidable. It was essential to found the pier on rock, and the depth was far too great for men to work under compressed air. A reinforced concrete cylinder, or monolith, with a steel cutting edge was designed and lowered into position on the bed of the river in November 1939. It was then sunk by open dredging, the walls being built up to keep them above water level. In April 1940, however, when 129 feet of cylinder had been constructed, the cutting edge suddenly broke through the subsoil and the monolith plunged down vertically for 53 feet and sank out of sight below water level. This indeed presented a problem! It was decided to build another length of cylinder and land it on top of the sunken section and join the two lengths together by means of reinforced concrete placed under compressed air. With great skill and care this was successfully accomplished, and the cylinder was extended to a length of 199 feet before sinking was resumed. In September 1941 it took another 'run' of 30 feet, and in June 1942 a third and last plunge of 28 feet, which landed the cutting edge on a heap of large boulders. The work of removing the boulders and excavating the rock was carried out by the Department of Main Roads separately from the contract. Charges of blasting gelatine up to 5 lb. in weight were used. After ignition of the fuses, the charges were dropped down a 4 inch tube into borings in the rock and exploded. When a solid foundation had been reached, the bottom was cleaned up and concreted.

Incidentally, this monolith and that for one of the piers on the cantilever span of the San Francisco-Oakland Bay bridge are the two deepest ever sunk. In the Hawkesbury river foundation the cutting edge reached a depth of 233 feet and excavation was carried to a depth of 241 feet 4 inches below low water. In the Bay bridge pier, the cutting edge was sunk to a depth of 228 feet and the maximum depth of excavation was 242 feet below sea level.

*   *   *

The Lower Zambesi bridge in Portuguese East Africa is another triumph of British engineers. It has a total length of 2¼ miles and is the third longest bridge in the world, only exceeded by the Chesapeake Bay bridge and the James river bridge in the United States. Designed by Messrs. Livesey & Henderson and Messrs Rendel, Palmer & Tritton, and built by the Cleveland Bridge Company of Darlington, it consists of thirty-three spans of 262 feet, 7 of 165 feet, and numerous shorter approach spans. It carries a single track of the Trans-Zambesia railway over the river about 200 miles north of Beira, to link up with the Nyasaland Railway. The total cost of the bridge and connecting railways was a little over 1½ million pounds. It was financed by the British Government, to assist in the development of the East African Colonies, and is to revert to the Portuguese Government in the year 2011.

Work began in 1930 on the building of the camp at Dona Ana. The site was infested by malarial mosquitoes and the contractors sought the advice of the Ross Institute on the anti-malarial measures to be adopted. Paraffin was sprayed on pools or any stagnant water where mosquitoes might breed, and wherever possible such pools were drained away. Efficient systems of sanitation were installed. To keep down flies and the infections they carry all slaughtering was done in a fly-proof abattoir. The verandas and windows of the staff bungalows were enclosed in mosquito-proof wire gauze. By adopting all these precautions, assisted by the use of insecticides, quinine, and mosquito-proof nets and boots, the camp was kept remarkably healthy. In five years only one case of malaria developed amongst the home-staff at site. For obvious reasons prophylactic medical treatment for the African labour was impracticable, but owing to the other anti-malarial measures taken, there was little incidence of the disease amongst them during the contract.

The caissons for the foundations of the bridge were sunk either on sandbanks in the dry season or from floating craft in the river. The system devised by H. J. Fereday (see p. 105) of sinking by means of open dredging was adopted, with provision for the use of compressed air if necessary. It proved successful and economical; most of the wells were founded in the sand at depths ranging up to 120 feet below low water level; pneumatic sinking was only employed on the few wells which were founded on rock. Moreover, all the piers were kept remarkably well to position and very little settlement was subsequently observed.

The steelwork was erected by means of Goliath cranes which ran on light service spans supported on temporary timber dolphins. All the steelwork of the thirty-three main spans was fabricated in the contractor's shops in England, steel-bushed[1] jigs being used for drilling the rivet holes at connections. The result was found to be so accurate that corresponding members were interchangeable in any span. In fact only the first two and the last two spans were assembled for trial in the yard prior to shipment to site. In March 1935, a month before contract time, the bridge was completed and opened to traffic. And for the first time a through route was provided, without reliance on ferries, for the produce of Nyasaland to reach the coast at Beira.

Reference must be made to an extraordinary attack by bacteria on the paintwork of this bridge. The steel had been cleaned by scraping and wirebrushing, and it was given one coat of paint in the shops and two more after erection at site. After thirteen of the main spans had been painted it was observed that patches of black powder were appearing on the surface, four or five months after the paint had been applied. The patches steadily increased in size and therefore the painting was stopped and samples of the powder and paint were sent to London for chemical examination. It was found that the oil in the paint had been attacked by airborne fungus spores and bacteria; these had infected the oil and ultimately broken down the paint, leaving the black powder residue. The bacteria are not peculiar to this part of Africa but are also to be found in Malaya and parts of India, where similar conditions of temperature and humidity prevail. After months of experimental work a paint was produced which proved resistant

[1] Templates in which hard steel bushes are inserted at each rivet hole; they have a longer life and give greater accuracy than jigs without bushes.

to the attack of these organisms. This has since been applied to the bridge and proved successful.

The protection of steelwork in tropical climates is not an easy problem. Even if there are no bacteria to attack the paint, the intense heat of the sun tends to dry out the oil and cause 'chalking'. A protection which proved effective on the New Howrah bridge in India was two coats of red lead to protect the steel from corrosion followed by two coats of aluminium paint to protect the red lead.

Another danger to which bridges in tropical countries are exposed is illustrated by the failure of the old Chiromo bridge, over the Shire river in Nyasaland, which was washed away in 1948. After an exceptionally high flood season, masses of sudd and islands of vegetation were broken away from the river banks and the shores of Lake Nyasa and came floating downstream. The sudd piled up against the piers of the bridge and blocked the 80-foot openings between them. As the floods continued, more sudd came down; whole islands with palm trees on them, features of the landscape, came floating round the bend. At last the pressure proved too great; the old piers gave way, and the sudd surged triumphantly onwards, bearing the steel spans of the bridge on top of it for a quarter of a mile before they sank to the river bed.

*   *   *

In 1850 construction started in India on the first two railway lines at Calcutta and Bombay; twenty years later they were linked at Jubbulpore and the 1,000-mile width of the continent had been crossed. Before the British left India they had constructed a network of lines more than 40,000 miles in length. The most formidable obstacles to the railways were the rivers, of which there are fifteen great ones and many lesser; most of them have now been bridged in two or three places. In the period from 1850 to 1940 something like a hundred major railway bridges over 1,000 feet long were built, compared with little more than a dozen of comparable size in Great Britain.

Owing to similarity of conditions encountered, a technique was developed that can be recognized all over the sub-continent. Bridge builders learned how to make do with the simplest kind of plant; they had to study and develop the use of guide banks to keep the rivers under the bridges; and they contrived to sink the deepest foundations that had ever been constructed, in order to prevent them from being undermined when the sand of the river beds was scoured away during the floods. An embarrassing habit of seasonal rivers that flow through sandy or silty soil is that of changing their course from year to year. Pre-eminent among such are the Yellow river in China, the Missouri in America, and the Ganges in Bengal. The Ganges in particular is a most erratic river, extremely difficult to keep under control. In some of its wanderings it washed away the railway station at Goalundo on the Eastern Bengal Railway; later on it adopted different tactics and left the station at Kushtea, which had been on its banks, stranded in the country seven miles away. Before engineers could bridge rivers like this they had to decide not only where to put the bridge and how long to make it, but also how to keep the river there! This study led to the development of bunds or training walls designed to maintain the river permanently in one channel, at any rate until it had safely negotiated the bridge. The pioneers in this work were J. R. Bell, after whom the well-known 'Bellbund' was named, and Sir Francis Spring, one time Chief Engineer to the Public Works Department of India, whose paper on 'Indian River Training & Control' has long been a classic.

A further problem was the enormous depth to which some of the rivers scoured out their beds in the flood season. It was estimated that the Ganges swept its sand bed away to a depth of 100 feet every year. During the floods, steamers that had foundered in the Ganges have disappeared without trace in the moving river bed and could never be recovered.

One of the most ambitious of the Indian bridges was the Lansdowne bridge built over the Indus at Sukkur (1889). This bridge had a clear span of 790 feet and until it was eclipsed by the Forth bridge was the longest of its kind in the world. It has an extraordinary appearance to us to-day; the braced lenticular[1] struts are reminiscent of crane jibs; the immense height of the cantilever arms dwarfs the shallow suspended span. Some of the Indian bridges are of great length. Of two bridges carrying the East Indian Railway over the Sone river, the upper one has twenty-eight spans of 150 feet and the lower one ninety-three spans of 100 feet. The lower bridge thus has a length of nearly two miles; the mental picture of a succession of ninety-three spans, the far ones disappearing into the heat haze across the river, makes one feel almost dizzy.

The story of the Empress bridge that carried the main-line railway over the Sutlej river illustrates the difficulty of the early engineers in knowing how long a bridge must be made. The first

[1] Convex-sided, or cigar-shaped.

bridge consisted of sixteen wrought-iron spans of 257 feet and was completed in 1878. Some years later, however, it became apparent that its length was excessive. By that time engineers had gained experience in the construction and effect of training walls, and it was decided to build guide banks to contain the river in about half the existing width and to shorten the bridge. In 1929 the work was finished and was completely successful. The river was contained in half the previous channel and the eight surplus spans were modified and re-used in a new bridge over the Ravi river.

As a typical example of these Indian bridges let us look at the history of the famous Hardinge bridge. This is a double-track railway bridge with fifteen spans of 345 feet and six short approach spans which carries the main line of the Eastern Bengal Railway over the Lower Ganges at Sara, about 110 miles north of Calcutta. Before the bridge was built the mounting traffic in jute and tea between Calcutta, Darjeeling, and Assam had all to be transhipped at the crossing and ferried over. This caused intolerable delays. By 1908 the chaos could be endured no longer, and the Government sanctioned the construction of the new bridge. It was designed in England by Sir Alexander Rendel and E. E. Robertson, and the bulk of the work carried out departmentally[1] at site.

Records showed that since 1868 the Ganges had moved eastwards at the bridge site a distance of 1¾ miles, at a rate of about 200 feet per year. Thus the first necessity was to construct training walls to maintain the river in a constant position. To do this a pair of stone pitched guide banks were built at the bridge site, and the headlands at two bends of the river a few miles upstream were revetted with rock. A depth of 150 feet was adopted as safe for the foundations of the bridge in mid-stream, but the two end piers, where the greatest scour was to be expected, were made 10 feet deeper.

Preparations were begun for obtaining the enormous quantity of stone, more than 1½ million cubic yards, required for pitching and for making concrete. Bengal is notoriously short of building materials and much of the stone had to be got from quarries more than 200 miles away. Land was acquired, steamers and river flats engaged, a camp built, workshops erected, services laid on, temporary railways constructed, and the necessary rolling stock and locomotives found. Before the end of the contract 81 miles of service track, 24 locomotives, and 830 wagons were in use. Two power stations were built to supply electricity for the work. The

[1] By direct labour and not by contract.

camp became a township with brick bungalows for the European staff, a market, hospital, and dispensary. A piped water supply was installed and electric lights and fans. Before very long some 24,000 Indians were employed in the quarries and at the site, and stone was being steadily delivered to the guide banks by rail and steamer.

The setting out of the bridge presented unusual difficulties owing to the hot climate and the width of the river; even in the dry season sights more than 3,000 feet long across the water were entailed. Surveying in hot countries is not easy, and an inexperienced engineer will quickly be caught out. The best time of day for taking readings on dumpy levels or theodolites is about 3.30 p.m. The image appears to be shimmering in the heat; it dances in the waves of the mirage, but it dances in one place and more accurate results are obtainable then than immediately after sunrise. For although in the early morning there is no mirage, and the image appears to be steady on the cross hairs of the instrument, after a few minutes it may slowly diverge.

The lower part of the wells, or monoliths, for the foundations of the bridge piers, were of steel. They were assembled, floated out, and sunk in position between pairs of pontoons anchored in the river. As the sand was grabbed out of the shafts by means of 100-cubic-foot dredges, the monoliths sank and the walls were built up of pre-cast concrete blocks. It was found that the best method of sinking was by 'running the wells'. In this operation, after the sand had been grabbed out to just below the level of the cutting edge, the water level inside the well shaft was lowered by pumping. This not only reduced the buoyancy of the well but also appeared to reduce the skin friction between the sand and the concrete walls by inducing a flow of water down the sides of the well and up into the shaft. It resulted in the quick sinking of the well a number of feet, and a certain amount of sand entering the well shaft. Dredging was then begun again and the operation repeated.

In built-up areas this method should not be used as it obviously disturbs the ground around the foundation and might affect the stability of nearby buildings. But in the Ganges, where the whole river bed is shifted to a depth of 100 feet every year, there is no objection to it.

By 1913 all the foundations of the Hardinge bridge had been built, the pier shafts constructed, and erection of the steel spans begun. The fifteen main spans, which were all fabricated in Great Britain, weighed 1,250 tons each. Some of them were erected in the dry season on timber staging, others were built over water on a service girder. This consisted of a much lighter steel span, capable of carrying the weight of one of the main spans and the erecting plant. It was floated out on two pontoons and placed in position between each pair of piers in turn, where it remained whilst the permanent steelwork was assembled on top of it; then the service span was lowered and floated out again to be used in the next position.

The last main spans were shipped after the first world war had broken out; they were despatched from Liverpool in fast liners and had to run the gauntlet of the cruiser *Emden* in the Indian Ocean. They got through safely but three of the 75-foot approach spans were less fortunate; two of them were taken by the enemy in Luxemburg and the third was interned at Port Said. These short spans, however, were comparatively easily replaced. The total cost of the bridge, including land and permanent way, was about 35,000,000 rupees (about 2¾ million pounds) and it was opened to single line traffic in 1915.

We have not yet come to the end of the story of the Hardinge bridge however; the Ganges was not going to submit so easily. At the bridge site its main channel was flowing hard up against the left or east guide bank. Three miles upstream of this point the river began its attack on the northern end of the Sara revetment; the end of this bank had been turned well inland, but the river moved eastwards and cut into the unprotected bank beyond the pitching. Between 1925 and 1931 the water increased its inroads at this point until the end of the Sara revetment, in spite of constant re-pitching, was cut off and swept away. The river then poured into the embayment it had made; its eddies swirled round in a pool 800 feet across, scouring out potholes 170 feet deep. Worse than this, however, the main stream was deflected across to the far bank and began to cut a breach there, two miles above the bridge.

To counter this move, the engineers curved back the end of the Sara revetment and built another 4,000-foot length of guide bank opposite it, at Damukdia, to prevent the threatened breach. The new guide bank provided for a scour of 160 feet; it took more than a million cubic yards of earth and boulders and was completed at a cost of £150,000. It was then thought that as the moves of the river both east and west had been countered, the danger was past. Anyone who believed that, however, was reckoning without the Ganges. Towards the end of the floods in 1933, the river suddenly began a rapid and abnormal rise. On the night of 25 September the watchman patrolling the banks reported that all was well, but next morning a villager going to work at 5 a.m. noticed that there was water behind the right guide bank. To the consternation of the engineers, this was found to be true. The river had breached the guide bank in the night at a point 1,800 feet upstream of the bridge (Fig. 19).

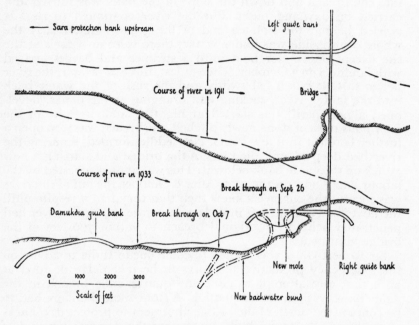

FIG. 19. A plan of the river Ganges above the Hardinge bridge, showing the course of the river when the bridge was completed, its course in 1933, the growth of the breach in September and October of that year, and the subsequent protective works.

In an hour or two it had swept away 400 feet of the bank, isolating a length at the end, and was sweeping out a deep embayment behind it. Unless it could be checked the river would quickly cut its way clean through behind the abutment of the bridge and wash it out. Ballast trains and labour gangs were immediately summoned, but little could be done, until they arrived next morning, except watch the river in its attack. An observer states that the river seemed to pour into the breach in rushes every two minutes, great waves tearing strips of land covered with jungle and trees from the disintegrating banks. So it continued until midday, when the attack slackened, and by 4 o'clock in the afternoon it had ceased and the pool behind the breach, which now measured 700 feet by 1,400 feet was calm. But the end of the gap had encroached 600 feet nearer to the bridge.

Next morning the ballast trains began to arrive, and pitching into the breach and down the slope of the bank was started and carried on day and night. But the river continued to rise. It swirled behind the isolated end of the guide bank; nearly the whole countryside was under water; there were no vessels at the site except one motor boat until a steamer and barges arrived with boulders on 3 October. Then at last, three days later, the river began to fall; but it fell swiftly and the rush of the water back into the falling river, sucking and dragging at the banks, developed a new peril; this started at nightfall and, in spite of the enormous mass of stone newly pitched, the breach was torn open a further 600 feet in a few hours. New eddies formed, scouring the river bed deep around the piers of the bridge and starting a new attack on the guide bank below it. This was at once arrested by the labour gangs now on the spot. After 8 October the fall of the river was steady; the engineers knew then that they had a respite until the next flood season; but in its last desperate attack the river had penetrated behind the original breach to within 700 feet of the bridge abutment!

Sir Robert Gales was invited to come out to India to advise on the emergency protective measures to be taken. He decided at once that any attempt to close the quarter-mile breach in the guide bank was out of the question. A stone mole therefore had to be constructed north of the bridge abutment to protect it; a backwater bund was to be built connecting the downstream end of the isolated piece of guide bank with the mainland; and in addition to these principal safeguards, a great quantity of heavy pitching was to be placed around the threatened piers of the bridge.

There was only a period of six or seven months to complete all this work before the next year's floods began, so it was urged on with all speed. Good progress was being made when, on 9 April 1934, one of the coolies went down with cholera. Three days later twelve men had died and 2,000 of the labour force absconded. The doctors worked twenty-four hours a day trying to get the epidemic under control. By the ninth day 2,000 more men had absconded and the death roll had risen to 74. And then when the situation appeared hopeless and it looked as if the bridge was foredoomed, the epidemic was halted. The coolies returned to the camp and the protection works were finished a day before the floods started on 13 June. The banks were lit with floodlights by night, and day-and-night patrols were organized. Every flood season from that day until now the banks of the Ganges have been patrolled at the bridge site. The protection works have proved effective and the vigilance of the patrols has averted any further crisis. The bridge still stands; but some who know the Ganges might say that the river bides its time.

Two technical developments of particular interest to engineers may be ascribed to India and are the work of the late H. J. Fereday, although they may have appeared in other forms elsewhere. In order to combine the advantages of open dredging and sinking by means of compressed air, Fereday devised a new method for the foundations of the Kalabagh bridge (1930) over the Indus. The caissons were designed for sinking by open grabbing, but provision was made for fixing a dome or roof to the working chamber at any time, so that compressed air could be applied if necessary. Thus the wells could be sunk quickly and cheaply through the sand by open dredging and when rock was encountered compressed air could be applied for that part of the work. This method was used successfully on a number of bridges in India and elsewhere, including the New Howrah bridge in Calcutta, the Silver Jubilee bridge over the Nerbudda river, the Ava bridge in Burma, and the Lower Zambesi bridge in Portuguese East Africa.

The other development to which we have referred consisted in pre-stressing the members of the main trusses. As this is a highly technical matter, however, of interest only to specialists in steelwork, further particulars need not be given here.

* * *

Another fine bridge in the Far East is the Ava bridge in Burma; comprising nine spans of 350 feet it carries the railway and road over the great Irrawaddy river close to Mandalay (Pl. 15). All except one of the foundations were sunk under compressed air and founded on rock at depths ranging up to 80 feet below water level. Built by the Hindustan Construction Co. of Bombay, they were at the time the deepest foundations sunk under compressed air in the East. The superstructure was fabricated in India and erected by Messrs Braithwaite & Co.

In 1933 the bridge was completed at a cost of just over one

million pounds. It was called the Ava bridge in commemoration of 'The City of Precious Gems', which had been in past centuries the seat of Government in Burma, the ancient Kingdom of Ava. Like most other bridges in Burma the Ava bridge was put out of action in the late war. Two spans were blown off the piers into the water before the bridge fell into the hands of the Japanese. Unfortunately, the troubled state of the country has so far delayed its repair[1].

The only other bridge of exceptional interest in Burma is the steel railway viaduct at Gokteik, built by an American company on a branch line in 1901. This was a fine bridge, sweeping in a wide curve across an 800-foot deep gorge in beautiful wooded country. It was carried on steel trestles, some of which were more than 300 feet high. The bottom of the gorge was spanned by a natural rock arch on top of which the bridge trestles were founded. The viaduct was bombed a number of times by the Allies but finally destroyed by the Japanese during their retreat in 1945. Since then new steelwork has been shipped from England and the bridge has now been rebuilt.

*   *   *

South-east of Burma lies the prosperous happy-go-lucky kingdom of Siam, peaceably-minded and powerless to resist the Japanese invasion in 1941. In Bangkok the pleasant shaded streets, running beside the waterways, are thronged with Siamese, Indians, and Chinese. And in the high-walled Palace City the priests, who still educate and dominate the people, dwell in their fabulous temples worshipping the images of Buddha.

There are a large number of railway bridges in the country, most of them unhappily destroyed in the war, which were originally supplied or built by British engineers. The Bandara bridge (1907) over the Menam river in the north was designed by Max am Ende as a cantilever bridge 861 feet long (Pl. 16). In the south is the Surat bridge of three spans totalling 664 feet over the deep, swiftly-flowing Tapi river, a few miles from Bandon. On the outskirts of Bangkok is the Rama VI bridge of five spans with an overall length of 1,455 feet. This was built by the French firm, Daydé of Paris, and opened in 1927. In the centre of the city is the fine Memorial roadway bridge, with an opening bascule span over the wide Chao Phya river. When war came to Siam all these

---

[1] Two new spans were fabricated by Braithwaites in 1951-52, but at the time of writing have not yet been erected. (Jan. 1953).

bridges were put out of action by Allied bombers. In 1948 the Siamese State railways placed a contract with this country for the reconstruction of the three biggest bridges, Bandara, Surat, and Rama VI, all of which have now been rebuilt with British steel.

Chapter 9

REINFORCED
CONCRETE BRIDGES

'Where economic law reigns supreme and mathematical exactness
is joined to daring and imagination: that is beauty.'

LE CORBUSIER

REINFORCED CONCRETE has only recently been applied extensively
to bridge construction, but so quickly did it win popularity that
it has been suggested that the last forty years might well be called
the 'Reinforced Concrete Age'. Many of the engineers who used
the new material failed to realize the originality in design which
it demanded. They employed it as though they were still working
in masonry or steel and used the established forms suited to
those materials. But there were a few pioneers who quickly saw
the way ahead. Foremost amongst these were Robert Maillart of
Switzerland, François Hennebique and Eugène Freysinnet of
France. Maillart was perhaps the first to show that the basic
element in reinforced concrete was the slab and not the beam,
post, or tie as in steel construction; Hennebique moulded his
bridges in sweeping curves in three dimensions; Freysinnet will
always be known as the pioneer of the modern system of pre-
stressed concrete.

Although the first patent for reinforced concrete was taken out
in England by Ralph Dodds as long ago as 1808, Portland cement,
which is the basis of the concrete of to-day, was not invented until
1824. It was then discovered by Joseph Aspdin, following up the
investigations of the Frenchman Vicat. Curiously enough the
first reinforced concrete objects on record were not made until
some forty years after Dodds had taken out his patent. Then two
Frenchmen, Lambot and Monier, made respectively a wire-
reinforced concrete boat and wire-bound flower pots! Some years
later Monier manufactured concrete railway sleepers and building
components; and although not an engineer he subsequently
played a leading part in reinforced concrete development.

This is not the place to explain the theory behind reinforced concrete, which is handled in numerous text books. The underlying idea is that the concrete takes compression, and steel reinforcement is incorporated to resist tension stresses that concrete could not withstand. The new material is therefore admirably suited to the construction of beam and arch bridges, but not, of course, to suspension spans where the main element is in tension. At first the working stress in the concrete was limited to about 600 and in the steel to 16,000 lb. per square inch. Improvements, however, in the quality of cement, the grading and mixing of concrete, and the introduction of vibrating by Freysinnet in 1920, have enabled the permissible concrete stress to be considerably increased. The vibrating of concrete by means of pneumatic or electric machines has now largely superseded hand ramming and tamping. It brings air bubbles to the surface and if properly controlled produces a dense strong concrete. The working stresses allowed by the authorities in Great Britain, however, are still substantially less than those adopted on the Continent. From the beginning France, Switzerland, and Sweden have been in the lead in concrete bridge design; it is their engineers who have contributed most to advances in technique and span, and they are still in the forefront to-day.

One of the reasons for the welcome accorded to reinforced concrete was that its advocates claimed that it would produce maintenance-free structures; it would not be necessary, as with steelwork, to clean and paint them every five to ten years. Unfortunately, however, experience shows that this claim is often not borne out in practice. There is no doubt that if the details of bridges are carefully designed and the construction is thoroughly supervised, little if any maintenance will be needed for a long time. But inspection of a number of existing bridges reveals a variety of defects; moreover, once the concrete begins to spall off and the steel reinforcement is exposed, the cost of repair will be very heavy, if indeed it is practicable at all. Hence the attention that engineers are giving to-day to the problem of control and elimination of cracks and the production of concrete with a solid weather-resisting surface. If cracks and all trace of honeycombs can be eliminated, then the danger from frost loses its terrors and the life of the bridge will be preserved. Another drawback is that few attempts to make concrete surfaces attractive in appearance, or to prevent their looks from deteriorating with age, have been successful.

Most of the early reinforced concrete bridges were simply

clumsy copies of steel or masonry structures. Engineers built
'through' spans[1] in which the heavy overhead chords and bracings
seemed to burden and oppress the roadway; in other designs the
very adaptability of concrete led to its undoing, and it was per-
verted into ugly and meaningless shapes intended to be decora-
tive. The first reinforced concrete bridge to be built in America
was not only surfaced to resemble stonework but was actually
hung with imitation concrete stalactites. Another more recent one
spanning a dual roadway was provided with concrete cutwaters
on the piers, presumably to divide the roadway traffic! Nearer
home, there is in Scotland an unhappy bridge which is a faithful
model in reinforced concrete of a self-anchored suspension span,
except that diagonal bracing is provided instead of vertical
hangers.

From the first, however, France produced designers of genius
such as Monier, Coignet, Considère, and Hennebique who did
not fall into these errors. In 1898 Hennebique designed and built
the first notable reinforced concrete arch, the Pont de Chatel-
lerault, with a span of 172 feet. A later bridge of his design is that
over the river Ourthe in Liège, built for the 1905 Exhibition.
This has a span of 180 feet and its graceful curves, slenderness, and
economy of material proclaim the master. It is axiomatic that a
good concrete design, in which every constituent is sparingly pro-
portioned and fully plays its part, will require less material than
an inferior design. But the workmanship needed and the skill in
casting thin slabs and shuttering[2] them to curves are of a much
higher order than that needed for massive concrete with flat surfaces. This may account for the general supremacy of French
designs over those of America and to a less extent Great Britain.
For in France skilled labour is relatively cheap and material
scarce; whereas in America labour is very expensive and concrete
and steel abundant. The dictates of economy encourage fine design only under the former conditions. There are however in
England and America some outstanding exceptions.

A fine example of the period up to 1930 is the Pont de la Caille,
an arch of about 450-foot span near Geneva. Spanning a deep
rugged gorge, the clean bold lines of the bridge, free from adorn-
ment, beautifully match its setting. But the verticals supporting
the deck are somewhat heavy and angular; and there is no obvious necessity for the massive dimensions of the uprights over the
springings. Another example is to be found in the famous Tun-

---

[1] Spans in which the greater part of the trusses is above roadway level.

[2] Building the timber moulds, or 'shutters', in which the concrete is cast.

hannock Creek Viaduct (1912-15) at Nicholson, Pennsylvania, which has a decided affinity with the Pont du Gard. Ten semi-circular arches of 180 foot span carry a double-track railway 240 feet above the waters of the creek. The deep spandrels are each pierced with eleven smaller arches. The massive symmetry of the design has a fine classical effect. The surface of the concrete was scored, however, to hide construction joints and to resemble the details of a stone arch. This attempted disguise, together with the rather heavy proportions show little faith in the ability of the new material to stand by its own merits.

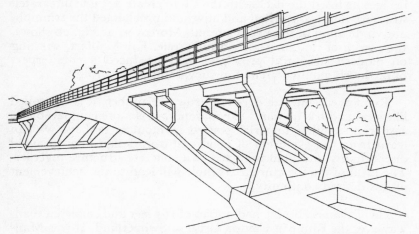

FIG. 20 Robert Maillart's three-hinged reinforced concrete bridge over the river Arve in a suburb of Geneva.

An interesting bridge built in England in 1928 is the Royal Tweed bridge, which carries the Great North Road over the river at Berwick. Designed by Messrs L. G. Mouchel & Partners and built by Messrs Holloway Brothers, this bridge has four arch spans ranging from 167 to 361 feet. Incidentally, the span of the longest arch is twice that of any previously built in Great Britain. The problem was difficult in that the ground level was consider-ably higher on one side of the river than on the other. The only proper engineering solution, therefore, involves a roadway on a gradient; and that in turn demands arches of increasing span as the rise becomes greater. The designers have cleverly avoided any break in continuity over the piers and have further integrated the structure by maintaining the spandrel posts and walls in one plane, slightly recessed behind the face of the deck and the arch ribs.

*   *   *

Robert Maillart, the champion of 'the structure as a whole', was born in 1872 and studied at Zurich; he was fortunate in his early days in working with Hennebique, and set up in independent practice in 1902. Three years later he built the Tavanasa bridge, the first of his famous three-hinged arches (Pl. 17). In these bridges he fused the deck with the rib to create a single integrated structure that was spirited and alive and proclaimed the triumphant vindication of the new material. Moreover, as Fig. 20 shows, the march of time had turned full circle. For Maillart, working on modern structural principles, had produced a counterpart of the lovely pointed arch of medieval times. He wrote:[1]

'Reinforced concrete does not grow like timber, it is not rolled like steel and has no joints like masonry. It is more comparable to cast iron, another material poured in moulds. Perhaps we can learn from the evolution of good cast-iron design how to avoid discontinuity and bind the parts of a concrete structure together. The ideal of the structure as a whole will lead to the achievement of this desired continuity.'

The Tavanasa bridge had a span of 167 feet and carried a roadway over the Rhine in Canton Grisons, Switzerland. It was Maillart's first masterpiece but was unluckily destroyed by a landslide in 1927. A few years later he was developing his mushroom-column construction and executed the first reinforced concrete building which had floors consisting only of slabs without any beams. In 1924 came the first of his stiffened slab arches, in shape like inverted suspension bridges and moulded with concrete of porcelain thinness. One of the most remarkable of these is the Schwandbach bridge, hidden in the forest near Schwarzenburg, which has a span of 111 feet (Pl. 18). This arch is actually built on a curved ground plan, and carries a roadway on a hairpin bend linking two sides of a deep ravine. The whole of the construction is in slabs, the thickness of the arched slab being less than 8 inches. The inner edge of this slab-arch follows the curve of the roadway; the outer edge is straight in plan and lies in a vertical plane.

[1] Translation by Author.

Maillart was undoubtedly many years ahead of his time, and his bridges, though none of them is of great span, incorporate courageous innovations that were not always acceptable to his contemporaries. One of his last and greatest projects was a continuous girder bridge to span the Rhône at Aire-le-Ville. This was to have a centre span of 246 feet and two side spans of 174 feet. But the two middle piers were designed as thin vertical walls instead of the sturdy supports that had customarily been adopted. These wall piers were intended only to resist vertical reactions, as the bridge was anchored at the ends. Unfortunately it was never built. It is of great interest to note, however, the similarity of these piers, or bearing walls, with those of the new Waterloo bridge which were designed at much the same time in England.

* * *

One of London's landmarks was John Rennie's fine old Waterloo bridge that was built in 1811-17 and opened by the Prince Regent, the Duke of Wellington attending. Seventy years later, concrete aprons were built to protect the foundations against scour and then, in 1924, when the bridge was more than a hundred years old, serious settlement occurred at one of the piers. Attempts to check the subsidence only made it worse; finally the traffic on the bridge was restricted, the arches on either side of the defective foundation were shored up, and construction of a temporary bridge was begun. Then the great controversy broke out as to whether the bridge should be demolished and replaced or reconditioned and widened. For thirteen years the dispute raged, almost as fiercely as the battle the bridge was named to commemorate. At long last Parliament approved the L.C.C. proposal for financing a new bridge, tenders were obtained, and work begun in October, 1937.

The new design was prepared by Messrs Rendel, Palmer & Tritton in association with the late Sir Pierson Frank; Sir Giles Gilbert Scott was the architect and Messrs Peter Lind & Co. were the contractors. The bridge provided a straight horizontal road for six lanes of traffic, carried on five spans double the length of the old ones, and so arranged as to offer the least possible interference with navigation at an awkward bend of the river (Pl. 19). But although to a lay observer the spans appear to be arches, springing from 14-foot wide piers, in reality they are not. Four of the five spans are in fact continuous girders, and the centre span consists of two cantilever arms and a suspended span. Moreover, the outer walls of the piers are simply shells which surround and protect bearing walls only 27 inches thick. These bearing walls extend for the full width of the four ribs on either side of the bridge, and carry the weight of the superstructure down to reinforced concrete foundations in the bed of the river (Fig. 21). The surrounding walls of the piers carry stops designed to prevent excessive movement of the superstructure. Moreover, they could be used as cofferdams for the purpose of inspecting and if necessary jacking the bearing walls in the event of settlement of the foundations.

An interesting feature of the construction was the successful attempt to control or eliminate cracks in the concrete. This was

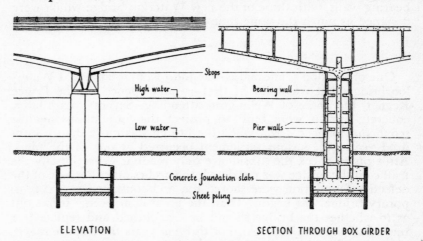

Stops

High water

Low water

Bearing wall

Pier walls

Concrete foundation slabs

Sheet piling

ELEVATION

SECTION THROUGH BOX GIRDER

FIG. 21. Two piers of Waterloo bridge, the right-hand one in section to show the internal bearing walls. The complete span of the arches is about twice the distance between the piers on the drawing.

done by using numbers of small-diameter reinforcing bars in the form of a mesh, welded at intersections; by adopting a carefully regulated mix of concrete, which was vibrated after placing; and by ensuring that the concrete was carefully cured, by keeping it moist and cool after it had set, in order to delay its shrinkage until such time as it was sufficiently strong to resist internal stresses.

The foundations of the bridge were built inside steel sheet pile cofferdams driven into the London clay. This method had been used previously on the new Chelsea bridge, and also on the bridges at Chiswick and Twickenham higher up the river. The Thames in

London is ideally suited to cofferdams and it is unlikely that pneumatic caissons, which were used for the Lambeth bridge (1932), New Southwark bridge (1921), and the Tower bridge (1894), will ever be adopted again. Cofferdams had been used in 1906 for the Vauxhall bridge but they were of timber, as the trough-shaped sections of steel piling that are commercially produced to-day were not then invented. The foundations of the original Waterloo bridge, like those of London bridge when it was rebuilt in 1831, were of timber piles and raft.

In its simplicity, elegance of line, and absence of decoration, Waterloo bridge is unique on the Thames. As soon as views of the new design were exhibited in 1934, the clamour against the replacement of the old bridge died down, but like all new things the proposed bridge was not universally admired. Bernard Shaw disapproved on the grounds that the design had some architectural merit whilst the buildings on the north bank had none—therefore the bridge would not do! Sacheverell Sitwell, possibly comparing the bare bones of the bridge with the lavishly decorated examples of earlier days, was much more forthright. He considered that the bridge 'means nothing, leads nowhere, and has no status, and no nationality.'[1] These criticisms are reminiscent of William Morris's attack many years ago on the Forth bridge. He said:

'There never would be an architecture in iron, every improvement in machinery being uglier and uglier until they reached the supremest specimen of all ugliness, the Forth bridge.'

Sir Benjamin Baker stood up for his bridge and expressed a doubt whether its critics really understood its anatomy or knew what they were talking about. The designers of the Waterloo bridge have other protagonists to speak for them. One of them[2] describes the bridge in lyrical terms:

'Long leaping curves are executed with such easy grace that the great new bridge, far from disfiguring the ancient face of London, brings it new life, new and exciting perspective. . . . Here is ample proof that distinguished twentieth-century architecture can take its place proudly in any setting.'

* * *

[1] *British Architects and Craftsmen*, 3rd Edition, 1946-7.
[2] Elizabeth B. Mock, *The Architecture of Bridges*, 1949.

In 1922 Eugène Freysinnet built his record span of 430 feet over the Seine at Saint Pierre du Vauvray. The narrow roadway was suspended by cables below two giant ribs which soared overhead. This bridge was blown in World War II and rebuilt, but before then Freysinnet had surpassed it in span by the Pont Albert Louppe over the river Elorn near Plougastel in Brittany. One arch of this bridge was also destroyed in the late war, but has since been replaced. The main crossing comprises three arches, each with a clear span of 567 feet. The bridge is classical in design and of particular interest in its method of erection. A timber arch centre, or staging, more than 500 feet long and 90 feet high was erected on shore and floated out on pontoons, the two ends of it being tied together by cables. This centre was supported on ledges at the springings of each arch in turn, so that it spanned the gap and enabled the concrete of the bridge to be placed. Freysinnet also took advantage of the increase in strength obtained by placing first of all the bottom slab of the arch concrete completely across the span, thus strengthening the centering before the remaining concrete was poured. After each arch had been concreted, a pioneer attempt was made, by jacking at the crown, to eliminate internal stresses which would otherwise be set up by the shrinkage of the concrete.

*   *   *

The longest reinforced concrete span yet built is the Sandö bridge in Sweden; this has an arch of 866 feet and would be long enough to span the width of the Thames at Westminster (Pl. 21). The bridge consists of a low arch rib with a rise of only 130 feet at the centre. The roadway runs over the top of the arch and is supported on pairs of circular columns. It was intended to place the concrete in moulds supported on timber centering which spanned the river without any support in midstream. This centre took the form of a timber-framed tied arch, with a span of 810 feet, which was made on shore and floated into position on two barges.

In August 1939, however, when the concreting of the bottom slab of the arch was nearly completed, the centering suddenly collapsed, fortunately during a break in the work. It had been made of sections of pinewood spiked together, and its failure was ascribed to the persistent damp weather and long loading period having reduced the strength of the timber. New centering was constructed in the form of a timber trestle built on thirteen groups of piles 130 feet long. Thereafter the concreting was successfully carried out in four stages: the bottom slab, the inner walls, the outer walls, and the upper slab. After each stage, stress was jacked into the concrete by means of twenty-four hydraulic jacks of 500-ton capacity, which were mounted in a special construction joint at the crown of the arch. By this means the centering was partially relieved of load and the bridge was successfully completed in 1943 (Pl. 20).

It represents a bold advance in design, as it is not only nearly one-third longer than the previous longest concrete span but, as will be seen from the table below, the thickness of the rib at the centre is very much less in proportion.

Bridge	Date of Completion	Span Feet	Ratio of Thickness : Span
Albert Louppe, France.	1930	567	1:40
Traneberg, Sweden	1934	585	1:60
Esla, Spain	1942	672	1:47
Sandö, Sweden	1943	866	1:100

Designed for the Swedish Highway Board under the direction of C. R. Kolm, the bridge was built by the Skanska Cement Co. of Stockholm at a cost of £335,000. It forms part of a long roadway viaduct and carries four lanes of traffic and two footpaths over the Angerman river. The arch rib is of triple cellular construction, the slabs and walls of which are all 12 inches thick. The overall depth of the rib is only 8 feet 8 inches at the crown, increasing to 14 feet 9 inches at the springings, where the ends are fixed. The bridge is noteworthy on account of the high stresses used in the design. The working stresses permitted in the concrete and steel were 1,550 and 21,200 lb. per square inch respectively, which are 24% and 28% higher than those adopted at about the same date for the Waterloo bridge.

Enthusiasts for reinforced concrete maintain that bridges could now be built in that material with arch spans up to nearly 5,000 feet. This would necessitate working stresses far higher than any in existing bridges but not, they maintain, higher than could safely be warranted. As long ago as 1928, Freysinnet proposed a reinforced concrete arch of 1,000 metre span (3,281 feet) for the

Hudson river. The ends of the arch were to be splayed out and anchored to skewbacks[1] in the rock; the roadway was to be suspended below a mighty concrete rib. It was claimed that the cost of this bridge would be less than half that of a steel span, and that it would have a greater factor of safety. Maybe this gives an inkling of what the future has in store, but if that is so, performance in reinforced concrete seems to be lagging behind that in steel. The longest single span in steel so far built is 4,200 feet which is in the ratio of 1 to 2.4 to the maximum theoretical span of (say) 10,000 feet for a roadway bridge. In reinforced concrete, however, the longest span built is 866 feet, as we have seen, which is a much smaller proportion of the suggested maximum span.

*   *   *

The most recent development in reinforced concrete is that of pre-stressing. In this system the steel reinforcement in the concrete is tensioned by means of screws or jacks, so as to put the concrete initially into a state of compression. Considère was possibly the first exponent of this idea. To anchor a stone structure exposed to breaking waves, he grouted steel bars into the rock and held the stones in place by tensioning the bars by means of threaded nuts. Freysinnet, however, has done more than any other engineer to develop and popularize the system. In 1934, immediately after it had been completed, the fine new maritime railway station at Le Havre began to settle and crack due to subsidence of the ground. The building, which was of reinforced concrete, seemed destined for total collapse; then Freysinnet offered to save it by using his process of pre-stressing. The method was so novel and its innovations so daring that it was only the absence of any other choice which allowed it to be attempted. In the event, Freysinnet's method proved to be a brilliant success; the station was saved and pre-stressed concrete was launched on the engineering world.

As mentioned above, the system consists in creating an initial compressive stress in the concrete. This pre-stress is usually made greater than the tension stress that would otherwise be developed under full dead and live load. The method can be applied to concrete whether it is poured at site or pre-cast. Freysinnet has made ingenious use of pre-cast concrete sections, building arch ribs of pieces of convenient size which have been cast in a works. These sections are placed end to end and a series of parallel high tensile steel wires, with an ultimate strength of 100 tons per square

[1] Abutments with a sloping face for the base of the arch to rest against.

inch, are inserted through holes left open in the concrete. The joints are then mortared and the wires tensioned so as to compress the sections together. If there are two or more ribs, transverse tensioning wires are also used. By this means it is possible to save about a third of the volume of concrete that would otherwise be necessary.

The devotees of pre-stressing claim that a much smaller factor of safety need be allowed in the wire than is customary in other forms of construction. The working stress they adopt is about 65 tons per square inch, (i.e. seven times that used in mild steel reinforcement) so that the weight of steel is reduced by at least

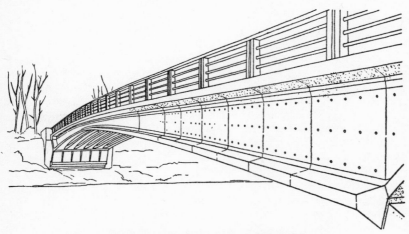

FIG. 22. The pre-stressed concrete bridge at Esbly.

three-quarters. As might be expected the resulting structures are not only highly economical in materials but also striking in their slender proportions.

During the second world war, the method was used in a large number of bridges that needed urgent reconstruction in Tunisia. As there was hardly any timber available for shuttering or steel for reinforcement, pre-cast concrete blocks were made and subsequently assembled by the Freysinnet system of pre-stressing. Since then numerous fine slender pre-stressed bridges have been built, amongst them the Esbly bridge over the river Marne, (Pl. 25, Fig. 22), the Fontaine bridge at Grenoble, the multi-span Galion bridge at Rio de Janeiro and others of lesser span in many countries.

On account of the thinness of the wire used, it is most important that it should be completely protected against corrosion. The necessity for the elimination of cracks in the concrete and the production of a dense flawless surface is thus once more underlined. At the time of writing the spans built are very modest, none being much longer than 300 feet[1]. It is too early yet, of course, to make any predictions as to the permanent value of a new method of building that has been so little tried and tested. But in a world of grave though passing shortages, such an economical system has a fine chance of development.

[1] Three bridges designed by Freysinnet and now under construction on the new Caracas-La Guaira highway in Venezuela have spans of 499, 479, and 452 feet respectively. The decks of these bridges are pre-stressed longitudinally and laterally, and pre-stressing cables are employed temporarily to relieve the arch ribs during erection. (May 1953.)

Chapter 10

THE CANTILEVER ERA

'Of the numerous practical considerations and
contingencies to be duly weighed and carefully
estimated, before the fitness of a design for
a long-span railway bridge could be satisfactorily
determined, none are more important than those
affecting the facility of erection.'

BENJAMIN BAKER, *Long-Span Railway Bridges*, 1867

THIS AND the next two chapters are devoted to a description of
some of the greatest modern cantilever, arch, and suspension
bridges. Each type of bridge has a maximum span beyond which
it would have insufficient margin of strength to support the weight
of traffic in addition to its own weight. For arch and cantilever
bridges the limiting span to-day is between 2,000 and 2,500 feet.
As stronger steel is produced so the maximum possible span increases. Suspension bridges, however, on account of the superior
strength:weight ratio of steel wire cables compared with structural
steel, can be built up to much greater spans.

Arch and cantilever bridges came into general use for long
spans in the railway era, when engineers found that structures
more rigid than suspension bridges, as then built, were needed to
carry railway traffic. For in addition to its greater weight, railway
traffic imposes much heavier wear and tear on a bridge because
of the hammer blows from the locomotive, impact due to the
presence of joints and irregularities in the track, and the effects of
lurching, nosing,[1] and rocking of the engine. During the last
eighty years the weight of locomotives with tenders has risen from
35 tons to 140 tons in England and 200 tons in America. We must
not however confuse the weight of such heavy railway loads with
that of inter-urban electric trains or tramways, which are often
loosely called railways but are, of course, very much lighter.

[1] The sideways push of the flanges of the locomotive wheels due to the guiding
action of the track.

TABLE I.—CARRYING CAPACITY OF MAJOR BRIDGES

Bridge	Type	Capacity of deck	Date Completed	Span ft.	Average dead load per ft. (lb.)	Max. live load per ft. (lb.)
Quebec	Cantilever	2 railway tracks 2 footways	1918	1,800	46,000	11,000
New Howrah	Cantilever	2 tramways 6 lanes roadway 2 footways	1942	1,500	—	7,100
Hell Gate	Arch	4 railway tracks	1916	977.5	51,000	24,000
Sydney Harbour	Arch	4 inter-urban tracks 6 lanes roadway 2 footways	1932	1,650	57,800	12,000
Golden Gate	Suspension	6 lanes roadway 2 footways	1937	4,200	22,100	4,000
San Francisco-Oakland Bay	Suspension	2 inter-urban tracks 6 lanes light roadway 3 lanes heavy trucks	1936	2,310	18,700	7,000
George Washington	Suspension	8 lanes roadway (so far erected)	1931	3,500	39,000	8,000
Camden	Suspension	4 inter-urban tracks 6 lanes roadway 2 footways	1921	1,750	26,000	12,000

Table 1 shows the carrying capacity of major cantilever, arch, and suspension bridges. From this it will be seen that the weight of traffic (or 'live load', as it is called) on the four railway tracks on the Hell Gate arch bridge is double that carried by Sydney Harbour bridge or the most heavily loaded suspension span. Incidentally it may also be noted that none of the existing long-span suspension bridges carries heavy railway traffic.

The collapse of the Tay bridge gave engineers renewed respect for the forces of nature and made them think twice about any structure that was not rigid and able to stand four-square to the wind. With a few notable exceptions in America, it sounded the death-knell of suspension bridges for forty years, and ushered in the age of the great cantilevers. The first of these was the Forth bridge, the masterpiece of a great engineering genius and of a kind that will probably never be repeated. This was followed by the well-known Queensboro' bridge in New York and the Quebec bridge in Canada. Tragedy came at Quebec, when the first bridge crashed during erection and the suspended span of its successor was dropped bodily into the river as it was being hoisted into place. During the second world war another fine cantilever bridge was built—the New Howrah bridge in Calcutta—one of the great legacies left to India by British engineers.

*   *   *

The first design for a bridge to span the Firth of Forth was made by James Anderson of Edinburgh as long ago as 1818. It was to be a chain suspension bridge of three spans and, judging by its outline, would have had a very brief life. In 1881, the design for a cantilever bridge prepared by John Fowler and Benjamin Baker was adopted. It is a finely conceived structure. The succession of mighty balanced spans, consisting of sturdy trusses battered[1] out to a width of 120 feet at the piers, gives it an air of strength and permanence (Pl. 22).

The two main openings of the bridge are each 1,710 feet long, made up of two 680-foot cantilever arms and a 350-foot suspended span. The bridge carries a double railway track over the estuary and allows a clear headroom of 150 feet for shipping. Of the three main piers, two are founded on the shores of north and south Queensferry respectively, and the third on the island of Inchgarvie.

In 1882 a contract was let to Messrs Tancred, Arrol & Co. and work at site began. The foundations for the northern half of the

[1] Sloping from the perpendicular.

bridge were built on solid whinstone rock, which outcropped on the surface; on the southern half they consisted of wrought-iron caissons 70 feet in diameter, sunk under compressed air to depths varying from 63 to 89 feet below high water. This work was sub-contracted to M. Coiseau of Paris, an expert on pneumatic sink-ing, who had used the method extensively at the port of Antwerp and elsewhere. The caissons, which had working chambers 7 feet high roofed with iron girders, were built on shore, launched from slipways, towed to site, and anchored in position. Before launching the air locks were installed and part of the concrete and masonry was placed, giving a total weight of over 3,000 tons.

The work progressed fairly smoothly, except for the north-west Queensferry caisson, which ran into trouble from the start. At an exceptionally low tide during the Christmas holiday, the cutting edge embedded itself in the mud and the caisson tilted, became fast and, contrary to expectation, failed to rise on the next tide. At high tide the water rose 18 feet and flowed in over the top of the side plates, filling the caisson. It was impossible to reach the lower sluice valves to open them; therefore, as the tide fell, the caisson remained full of water and became top-heavy. Owing to its tilt, the centre of gravity was thrown further towards the low side, with the result that the caisson partially capsized and slipped 20 feet out of position. Efforts to pump it out, after divers had laboriously fixed more side plating, resulted in the plates giving way under the water pressure and tearing wide open. Ultimately, a sheathing of timber like a barrel had to be fixed by divers all round the caisson and securely strutted inside. Then the water was pumped out and, somewhat to everyone's surprise, the caisson suddenly rose out of the mud and floated again. This accident had delayed the work ten months, during which the other foundations were practically completed.

Much more experience of compressed air work had been gained by this time and, although the cause of 'bends' was still not clearly known, the proper treatment for it had been discovered, and men showing the symptons were promptly put back under pressure. As a result no lives were lost during sinking. There was an alarming incident, however, when the south-west Queensferry caisson was being sunk through a layer of soft silt. The cylinder suddenly plunged down, threatening to engulf the men inside it in the mud; with great presence of mind the foreman turned all the air compressors full on with the result that the silt was forced down inside the working chamber and the men escaped.

This was the first long-span railway bridge to be built of steel;

the material was still novel and comparatively untried, but its strength and 'workability' impressed all those who used it. It became the latest fashion, so much so that spiral steel shavings, instead of being thrown on the scrap heap, were galvanized and sold as trinkets. The Board of Trade specified that working stresses should not be more than a fourth of the ultimate strength of the steel used, but made no further stipulations. The engineers specified that the steel for tension members should have an ultimate strength of 30 to 33 tons per square inch and for compression members 34 to 37 tons per square inch. These figures are substantially higher than the strength of mild steel to-day, which is from 28 to 32 tons per square inch.

It was decided to design the main compression members as tubular struts; some of them were 350 feet long and had to be made 12 feet in diameter. The reason for this choice was that the circular section gives the greatest strength for the weight of steel employed and is therefore the most efficient for its purpose. But all the curved plates had to be bent hot in the shops in hydraulic presses. This method would not suit present shop practice, which is to fabricate rectangular sections built up of flat plates and square angles. But with the introduction of welding and other new methods tubular construction has fresh possibilities and offers great advantages. The tension members were designed as lattice girders. There was abundance of skilled labour available from the shipyards and therefore shipbuilding methods were adopted. The 51,000 tons of steelwork were erected at site piecemeal, individual plates and bars being lifted by 30-cwt travelling cranes, fitted in place, and riveted by means of hydraulic riveting cages. No fewer than $6\frac{1}{2}$ million rivets were used, from $\frac{3}{4}$-inch to $1\frac{1}{8}$-inch in diameter and up to $11\frac{1}{4}$ inches long.

The erection of the steelwork proceeded outwards from both sides of each main pier, so that the weights on either side were kept in balance. Repeated checks on the line and level of the ends of the cantilevers showed that all three of them tended to build towards the east. Whether this was due to the effect of the sun or the prevailing westerly winds is not known; but when completed the ends of all the cantilevers were 2 inches to the east of the centre line. The two halves of the suspended span were built out from the ends of the cantilever arm until they met, and the time came to make the junction at the centre. With considerable courage, the engineers had relied to a large extent on the effect of temperature to close the gap and permit the final central connection to be made.

It was calculated that at a temperature of 60°F. the steelwork would expand sufficiently to bring the bolt holes in the overlapping connection plates fair; so that the joints in the lower chord could be completed. Owing to delays however, the south span was not ready for closure until October—a month later in the year than expected; so that the required temperature of 60°F. was not likely to arise. However, 10 October was a sunny day, and in the afternoon the temperature had risen to 55°F.; with the help of hydraulic jacks, the holes in the west chord joint were brought fair and the closing bolts were driven. But a chilly north-east wind was blowing and the holes in the east boom remained stubbornly ¼-inch blind. At all costs the steel must be expanded to close the gap, and there was only one way to do it. For 60 feet on either side of the centre, wood shavings and oily waste soaked in naphtha were laid along the lower chord and set alight. In a few minutes the steelwork, heated by the flames, expanded the desired amount, the last holes came fair, and the bolts were inserted. Thus by adopting the opposite procedure from that at St Louis, where the chords were packed in ice, the situation was saved. Next day the wedges to close the compression joints in the upper chords were driven, and the temporary ties at the ends of the suspended span were removed. In the following month the north span was closed and the bridge was tested by running onto it two trains 1,000 feet long weighing 1,800 tons. After successfully passing this test, the bridge, which forms an illustrious example of the works of the Victorian era, was opened by the Prince of Wales.

Westhofen in his report on its construction states:

'On Jubilee night [21 June 1887] although the atmosphere was somewhat thick, 68 bonfires could be counted at one time on the surrounding hills and isolated points, while the great masses of the central towers of the bridge, lighted up by hundreds of electric arc lights—Lucigen and other lamps—at various heights where the work was carried on, formed, with their long-drawn reflections in the waters of the Firth, three pillars of fire, and afforded a truly wonderful and unique spectacle.'

And now what of the men who designed and built the bridge? Sir John Fowler was born in 1817 and underwent his training at a time when the cheap production of iron made the whole world the customer of England. When he set up as a consulting engineer, the railway mania was sweeping the country and engineers were invited to work night and day on the preparation of plans and parliamentary estimates. Westhofen tells how Fowler was aroused one night by loud knocking on his door. A railway promoter had arrived by coach with £20,000 as payment on account if he would undertake the preparation of the plans for a new railway from Leeds to Glasgow! Engineers also had to give expert evidence in Committee, where they were examined by counsel advised by other engineers. At the same time there was excited speculation in the Stock Exchange. Operators on the market used to attend committees and buy or sell according to the fluctuation of the argument. To quote Westhofen again:

'Fowler once met an acquaintance rushing along the corridor of the House in the wildest excitement and when he stopped him to learn the cause, the man explained, "Don't detain me! Robert Stephenson has broken down in his attack and I am off to buy a thousand Great Northerns.'

Fowler went straight into the hurly burly of the railway world and was engaged on a large number of projects, including the Metropolitan Inner Circle in London and railways in Australia, India, and Egypt. On the death of Brunel he became consulting engineer to the Great Western, and in 1866 was elected President of the Institution of Civil Engineers.

Benjamin Baker was twenty-three years Fowler's junior. He was trained in an iron works in South Wales and subsequently entered Fowler's office in London, where he was engaged on the Underground railways. Amongst his many activities he designed the cylindrical vessel in which Cleopatra's needle was conveyed from Egypt. Subsequently he was consulting engineer on the Aswan Dam. But bridges were his principal interest and during his career he had the opportunity of strengthening three of Telford's masterpieces, the Menai, Buildwas, and Over bridges. His articles on 'Long-span bridges' were published in England, America, and on the Continent. He soon became the foremost bridge specialist of his day, and there is no doubt that his was the brain that conceived, and his the driving force that inspired, the Forth bridge project.

William Arrol, the contractor and founder of the Company that bears his name to-day, was born at Paisley. He was apprenticed to a blacksmith at the age of thirteen and a number of years later set up as a contractor with a capital of £85 which he had saved during that period. Speaking of this time subsequently he said, 'Whatever I went to I put my whole mind to'. As his reputation advanced, contract followed contract; he founded the Dalmarnock Ironworks in Glasgow and his Company became one of the leading manufacturers and builders of bridges. To the last, however, he was the practical engineer, taking his problems to the templatemaker rather than to the draughtsman; more at home on the bridge site than in the office. His Company carried out many important works, including the rebuilding of the Tay bridge, and Fowler and Baker had no hesitation in entrusting the construction of the Forth bridge to him. Both Benjamin Baker and William Arrol were knighted the year after its completion.

Of the workmen, Westhofen reports that 'they were a civil and well-behaved lot of men, always ready to oblige, always ready to go where they were told to go, cheerfully obeying orders to change from one place to another, and above all things, ready to help others in misfortune, not with advice but with hands and purses.' The largest number of men employed was 4,500 and the system of payment by piecework was adopted whenever possible. There were no fewer than fifty-seven fatal accidents, but most of them appear to have been due to carelessness or indifference. Any tool dropped from the height of the bridge might cause a fatal injury. Benjamin Baker noticed that a spanner dropped from a height of 300 feet knocked off a man's hat and smashed its way through a four-inch thick plank. One of the workmen elected to cross the bridge on an icy cold day by hauling himself hand over hand along a rope 100 feet up; the cold soon numbed his hands and he fell into the water, but was rescued. Perhaps the most extraordinary accident recorded was that of another man who contrived to drive a nail through his own hand!

*　　*　　*

The next big cantilever bridge to be built was the Queensboro' bridge over East River in New York City. It has two main spans of 1,182 feet joined by a central anchor span of 630 feet on Blackwell Island. This bridge is unusual in that the main spans each consist of two cantilever arms joined at their extremities, without any suspended span. Engineers will appreciate that it is therefore a highly indeterminate structure; a load on any part of it sets up stresses throughout all the spans, and the calculations must have been most laborious. The bridge is double-decked, and carries a huge volume of roadway and railway traffic. Shortly after the opening ceremony it was found that the dead load had been considerably underestimated. The authorities insisted on having all the calculations re-made; as a result many of the members were shown to be overstressed and part of the roadway had to be omitted in order to relieve the weight on the bridge.

* * *

In 1904 work began on the construction of the Quebec bridge over the St Lawrence River in Canada. The bridge had to carry two railway tracks, and was originally intended to have a main span of 1,600 feet. After the contracts for the foundations and super-structure had been let, it was decided on the advice of Theodore Cooper of New York, who had been appointed Consulting Engineer, to increase the span to 1,800 feet. The reason for this was to reduce the depth and size of the foundations; but it incidentally had the effect of making the bridge the longest single span in the world. The design specification was modified at the same time, but not in such a way as to reduce the strength of the bridge. With his many years experience and high reputation, Theodore Cooper was amongst the foremost bridge specialists of America. He was approaching seventy years of age, however, and his poor health rarely permitted him to leave New York. Unfortunately therefore, he was unable to visit the site at all during the erection of the steelwork.

All went well until the south anchor span and cantilever arm had been completed and the cantilevering out of the suspended span had begun. Then in August 1907 it was found that the steel web plates of some of the heaviest lower chord members near the tower were showing signs of buckling. There was some dispute about the matter, as it had been observed that these web plates were wavy to the extent of $\frac{3}{4}$ inch when the members left the shops. Cooper was informed of the buckling and the amazing thing is that only he, of all the engineers concerned, seems to have realized the gravity of the position—that here was the greatest bridge in the world and that it might well be on the verge of collapse! He gave instructions for further investigation with a view to straightening the webs, and was under the misapprehension that erection had meanwhile been suspended. However, the buckling swiftly increased from $\frac{3}{4}$ inch to more than 2 inches. In spite of this the erection crane was moved out onto the next panel and then, on the morning of 29 August, the crash came and 9,000 tons of steel went down with the men at work on it. Of eighty-six men on the bridge only eleven escaped. The anchor arm broke near the centre and the tall end-posts fell, to use the words of an eye-witness, 'as if they were ice pillars whose ends were rapidly melting away'. One of the survivors was a riveter named Beauvais who had been working inside the chords. His mate had found two rivets that they had driven within the hour broken by the buckling of the webs. Beauvais gave evidence at the subsequent enquiry:

'*Mr Holgate:*[1]   Can you account for these two particular rivets being broken? There were other rivets that may have been strained in the same way; why should they not have broken?

Mr Beauvais: Of course, I did not test them. If I had I would know just exactly what was broken and what was not, but while I was driving two or three other rivets, after that I found the first one broken off. He said "There is another one broken", and I tested it with a drift pin and it was broken off straight. You could turn the one end and the other end would be still. It was impossible to pull it out because it was plugged in there. There were two rivets broken. I called Mr Meredith, the rivet boss, and also to see that the ribs were bending in. He looked down there and told me that it was not any worse than the others. He did not think it serious.

Prof. Galbraith: The ribs were bending in?

Mr Beauvais: Yes. . . .

Mr Holgate: Having got to the point where you saw these two or more rivets broken, do you recollect anything between that and the collapse of the bridge?

Mr Beauvais: I guess not. I was driving rivets, and I was about to shoot another rivet when the crash came down . . . I was right inside the chord . . . When this chord landed it did not land on the ground. It stood three or four feet in the air. I held onto the chord and never touched the ground.

[1] The Royal Commission consisted of three members: Henry Holgate (*chairman*), J. G. G. Kerry, and Prof. J. Galbraith.

Mr Holgate: You were in what chord?

Mr Beauvais: No. 10, Montreal side. As soon as everything
                  was still, I came out. It was easy to stay
                  there because I was tight in there. I had one
                  leg broken and my nose was broken.'

One of the timekeepers, Huot, was 75 feet out on the anchor
arm when he heard a crack and saw the compressed air pipe burst
beside him; then, realizing what was happening, he ran for his
office, at the end of the bridge, with the deck opening under his
feet. The fact that he just got there tells us that the collapse probably took between five and ten seconds from start to finish.

As disclosed by the Report of the Royal Commission which
investigated the failure, the collapse was primarily due to the
spliced joints of the compression chord being allowed to remain
partly open and unriveted. The lacing bars on the chord were
also too weak to restrain the web plates from buckling. Besides
these immediate causes, however, other grave shortcomings were
disclosed. The specification was inadequate, the dead load of the
bridge underestimated, and the unit stresses permitted were too
high. Even if the span had been safely erected, it would not have
been strong enough to carry the traffic for which it was intended.
Nor was it practicable to re-use any of the remaining steelwork in
the reconstruction of the bridge, as it was decided that an entirely
new design must be made. This was entrusted to a Board of three
engineers of whom only Ralph Modjeski, who had had considerable experience in the construction of long-span bridges, served
until the end of the contract.

Two years were occupied in clearing the steel wreckage of the
first bridge from the south shore. Meanwhile an exhaustive series
of tests was made on the strength of riveted joints, eyebars, struts,
and tension members, both in mild and high-tensile steel. It was
finally decided to use nickel steel (at allowable stresses 40%
greater than for mild steel) for the whole of the main trusses.
These were to remain parallel but the width between them was
increased from 67 feet to 88 feet. Eyebars were used for all the
main tension members and pin connections for nearly all joints,
except those in the lower chords, which were riveted. K-bracing
was adopted in the trusses as it was considered to give greater
safety, economy, and rapidity in erection; and an entirely new
and much more stringent specification was prepared.

An effort was made to use the existing foundations by sinking
new caissons alongside, to enlarge them to the required size. The

new caissons were built (and it is surprising that Douglas fir was used, even at this late date, instead of steel) but the attempt was unsuccessful. It was then decided to abandon the existing foundations and build entirely new ones, which were located 65 feet south of the original piers. By 1914 the new foundations had been built. Compressed air was used, and there were few cases of bends, none of which proved fatal. A most efficient medical lock was provided, 7 feet in diameter and 20 feet long. It had two beds for patients and was supplied with heating coils, pressure gauge, thermometer, clock, electric light, and telephone.

The anchor arms of the bridge were erected first, on falsework, and the cantilever arms were then built out from either side. Huge travelling gantry cranes were used for erection of the steelwork. These cranes were electrically operated and ran on the bridge deck between the trusses; they were 190 feet high and weighed 920 tons—the heaviest cranes ever used for bridge erection. Each was equipped with four 55-ton and four 20-ton hoists, besides auxiliary light derricks of 5 and 10-ton capacity. By September 1916 the erection of the anchor and cantilever arms had been completed and it only remained to erect the suspended span. This had been built on the river bank, and it was intended to float it out on pontoons and lift it into position by means of hydraulic jacks. The span was 640 feet long and weighed 5,000 tons; it would have to be lifted about 130 feet. On 11 September it was safely floated out and towed to the site; the lifting links at the four corners were connected, and the raising of the span begun. At the third lift of 2 feet the scows floated clear and the span was left hanging on the links at the ends of the cantilever arms. After an interval for breakfast the lifting operations were resumed. Everything was going according to schedule when suddenly there was a loud report; a casting at one corner of the span had failed; that corner slid off its support, the span tilted, broke its back, and plunged into the water (Pl. 23). The worst feature of the accident was the loss of life entailed, thirteen men being killed and fourteen injured. The St Lawrence Bridge Company, who were contractors for the superstructure, at once advised the Government that they accepted full responsibility and would replace the span. It was found that the failure of a complicated cruciform casting had been responsible for the disaster. Within a year the span had been re-made and successfully erected (Pl. 24). The cruciform castings proved to be an unnecessary refinement and were replaced by compressible lead plates; the lifting occupied

four days. The deck was then completed and the bridge handed
over to the Government in August 1918.

*   *   *

Since the Quebec bridge a number of cantilever bridges have
been built in America with spans up to 1,400 feet; but the longest
single span is that of the New Howrah bridge over the Hooghly
river in Calcutta. This is the third longest cantilever bridge in the
world, only exceeded in span by the Forth and Quebec bridges.
Until it was opened in 1943 the only bridge in the city was Sir
Bradford Leslie's famous floating bridge built in 1874 and intended to last twenty-five years. Constructed principally of timber on
pontoons, and constantly under repair, it survived nearly three
times as long.

Day and night a constant flow of traffic and pedestrians poured
over it. Horse-drawn gharries, coolies pushing hand-carts, rick-
shaws, bicycles, taxis with bearded Sikh drivers, huge American
cars, white-coated traffic police and the unforgettable trains of
bullock carts, the timbers creaking under their loads, followed
each other in almost unbroken procession. On the footpaths,
thronged with people from most countries of Asia, lay beggars
clamouring for alms. Sacred bulls and cows roamed at large, slept
on the pavements, and fed out of the huge bins of garbage which
stood overflowing at the curb.

The Hooghly is a tidal river with a range of 20 feet, so that
hinged shore spans had to be provided at each end of the floating
bridge. At high water these became so steep that the coolies and
bullock carts could hardly negotiate them; long traffic jams were
caused, whilst heavy bullock carts were lowered slowly down the
slope one at a time, by means of a rope round a bollard. By 1933
the old bridge had become so inadequate and its upkeep so costly
that the Government of Bengal decided that it must be replaced.
Contractors were invited to tender on an official design prepared
by Messrs Rendel, Palmer & Tritton for a cantilever bridge of
1,500-foot span. This provided for a roadway 71 feet wide with
two 15-foot cantilevered footways. Quotations were received from
British, Indian, and German firms, and in 1936 the contract was
awarded to the Cleveland Bridge Company of Darlington, with a
strong recommendation that they used Indian-made steel. This
they agreed to do, and 23,500 tons out of a total of 26,500 tons was
supplied by the Tata Iron and Steel Company of Jamshedpur and
fabricated by the Braithwaite, Burn and Jessop Company at four

different shops in Calcutta. All major items of plant and the remainder of the steelwork, including many intricate items, were made in England. The total cost of the bridge and its approach spans finally amounted to nearly £2,500,000.

The first job was the construction and sinking of two huge monoliths, the biggest ever sunk on land, to form the foundations of the main piers. Measuring approximately 180 feet by 81 feet in plan (an area sufficient for four tennis courts), these were divided into twenty-one wells, each 20 feet square, surrounded by reinforced concrete walls 5 feet thick. As the monoliths were sunk, by grabbing the muck out through the wells, the walls were built up to keep them above the surface of the ground. All kinds of curious objects were brought up by the grabs. The steel cutting edge at the bottom of the monoliths crashed its way through old timber 'country' boats and their cargoes that had lain buried for hundreds of years in the soft silt and sand. Anchors, grappling irons, cannons and cannon balls, part of an idol, brass vessels and a variety of rupee coins dating back to the days of John Company were unearthed.

The staff at site was composed of British senior engineers and foremen with Indian assistants. The labour consisted primarily of Mohammedans and Hindus; Sikhs and Pathans proved to be fine riveters; steel erection was mostly done by Punjabis and Bombay Khalassies; Nepalis and Ghurkas were employed as watchmen. No trouble from labour or religious feuds was experienced throughout the six years of construction. Work was interrupted by a great number of Indian festivals. Amongst these are the Mohammedan Bakr-Id when cows are sacrificed and in December the fast of Mohurrum; there is also the delightful Hindu festival of Dewali when buildings are decorated with myriads of twinkling lights—as though a host of giant fireflies had descended on the city. The Indians show their appreciation of the machines they use, and on holidays, cranes, grabs, locomotives and even surveying instruments were hung with flags and bedecked with flowers.

The work of sinking the monoliths was carried on day and night and continued steadily at a rate of a foot or more per day. Forty Indian crane drivers had to be trained on the job, working in three shifts of eight hours each. At a depth of 87 feet below ground level the monolith on the Howrah side penetrated 7 feet into stiff clay; this was impervious to water, so that it was possible to pump the wells out in turn and plug them with concrete in the open. But on the Calcutta side, after making good progress through a

30-foot bed of silver sand, the monolith was held up by friction between its walls and the ground, and progress became rather slow and bumpy. By this time it had sunk 90 feet below ground and its weight was nearly 40,000 tons. The muck had to be grabbed out of the middle of the wells deep below the cutting edge in order to get the monolith to move. Suddenly one night, the ground below it yielded and the whole mass plunged down 2 feet or so, shaking the ground and the buildings around it. A Hindu temple at one end of the monolith was destroyed and had subsequently to be re-built; a warehouse at the other end sagged down, and it was said that the seismograph at Kidderpore had registered an earthquake! In spite of these difficulties the monoliths were kept remarkably true to position, the biggest departure of the top or bottom in any direction being only two or three inches.

Finally the Calcutta monolith was founded in blue clay at a depth of 103 feet and as the ground was not watertight, compressed air had to be applied to each well in turn to expel the water and to enable the foundations to be inspected and cleaned up before concreting (Pl. 28). This was a hazardous operation, as the pressure required to keep the water out at that depth amounted to more than 40 lb. per square inch. Men could work in it for only four-hour shifts, and unless the pressure was very accurately controlled there was danger of a 'blow' into one of the adjacent wells. The work of concreting under compressed air began in July after the rains had broken and was finished in November 1938. Although no fewer than 500 Indians of eight different denominations were employed on the compressed air work it was completed, thanks to the system of stage decompression adopted, with very little illness.

Meanwhile the twin monoliths for the anchorage foundations had been sunk at each end of the bridge. At the bottom of these foundations, heavy steel grillages were concreted in, to which the ends of the anchor arms of the bridge were connected by long vertical steel links. Reinforced concrete caps were then built on top of the main monoliths and the erection of the steel towers began. These were built by two 'creeper cranes' which were subsequently used to erect the remainder of the steelwork. Each crane weighed 610 tons and had two jibs capable of lifting 65 tons and of slewing right round.

The general erection scheme is shown in Fig. 23. The creeper cranes first built the anchor arms, which were supported on falsework. In doing so they had to haul themselves up a slope of more than 30° until they were in position to erect the upper parts of the towers. Section by section the steel towers were built until they stood 270 feet high; and so accurate was the fabrication and assembly that a survey of the Howrah tower after completion showed that the legs were free from twist and that the top of the tower was within $\frac{3}{64}$ inch of its correct alignment. In order to complete their connection, the tops of the towers had to be strained

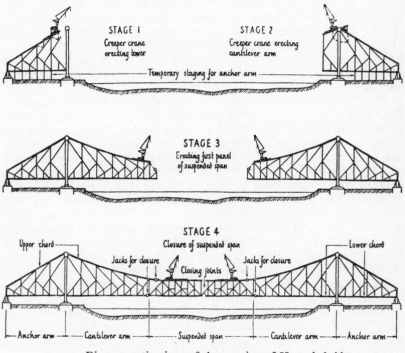

FIG. 23. Diagrammatic views of the erection of Howrah bridge.

back 13 inches towards the shore. As they were rigidly bolted down at the base, this required a force of some 140 tons and converted the towers temporarily into a kind of gigantic catapult; but fortunately they were never let go.

The creeper cranes were now standing just behind the towers. In this position the tops of the jibs stood nearly 500 feet above the ground. They were the highest land marks in Calcutta and had to be lit at night for safety of aircraft. The next and most difficult operation was to move the creeper cranes over the tops of the towers, so that they could start on their downward and outward journeys erecting the steelwork over the river. Each crane had been hauled up the anchor arm standing on a triangular-shaped cradle. The slope of the top of the cradle had been made similar to that of the bridge on the other side of the tower. The next move was to shift the hauling ropes from the cradle to the under-carriage of the crane. The crane was then simply lowered slowly down off the cradle and onto its tracks on the cantilever arm. The cradle was left behind and subsequently burned into pieces and removed.

Referring to Fig. 23, we have now reached the erection of the cantilever arms of the bridge, which were commenced at the end of 1940. By mid-summer they were completed, and by December 1941 the two halves of the suspended span had been built out until they met, except for a gap of approximately 18 inches at the middle. Then began the closure of the bridge by a method that had never before been attempted on such a scale. Each half of the suspended span was 282 feet long and weighed 2,000 tons. They were joined by moving the two halves horizontally towards each other, by means of hydraulic jacks, until the gap was closed and the connections at the centre could be permanently made. Like other major engineering operations, this could be exactly cal-culated and controlled and hence brought to a successful conclu-sion. But if any unforeseen misfortune occurred, the forces let loose could be so huge that they would at once 'take charge', with disastrous results.

The closure of the bridge was carried out by means of sixteen hydraulic jacks each of 800-ton capacity; these were arranged to work horizontally, eight of them at each end of the suspended span. The closing operation began at daybreak on 30 December 1941; telephones had been installed from the control point at the centre of the bridge to all the jacking points. The motors of the n° mps operating the jacks were started and the two half spans were steadily advanced towards each other until the bolt holes in the centre connections of the lower chords came fair. Quickly the bolts were inserted and tightened up by gangs of men trained in advance. A gap of half an inch still remained in the upper chord joints; this was next closed by running out the jacks in the top chords. But it was now after 9 a.m.; the heat of the sun was be-ginning to distort the steelwork and the joints had to be squeezed together with a load of 200 tons before the bolts could be inserted. Then, in successive stages, the pressure was released in all the jacks and by 1 o'clock the closure was completed and the suspended span freely supported and secure. The fact that in these few hours the length of the lower chord of the span had increased under strain by 4 inches whilst the length of the upper chord had decreased by a corresponding amount, gives some indication of the transformation that had taken place and the magnitude of the forces involved.

It is of interest that although the second world war broke out in the middle of the contract, the work was not delayed. Once again as on the Hardinge bridge in the first world war, pieces of steelwork sent from England had to run the gauntlet of enemy submarines and raiders. But no important item was lost.

The steelwork of the deck was completed, the roadway concreted, and the bridge finally opened to traffic in February 1943. The old floating bridge was then removed. A census made in May 1946 of traffic passing over the new bridge in twenty-four hours showed that it was used by 121,100 pedestrians (a crowd of Cup Tie proportions), 2,997 cattle, and 27,400 vehicles. The maximum number of vehicles using the bridge per hour was actually 20% higher than that on London bridge, which is the busiest in the metropolis.

Chapter 11

BIG STEEL ARCHES

'Like half a rainbow rising on yon shore
While its twin partner spans the semi o'er
And makes a perfect whole that need not part
Till time has furnished us a nobler art.'

THOS. POPE. *A Treatise on Bridge Architecture*, 1811

THE SUCCESS of the Eads bridge at St Louis encouraged the construction of arch bridges in Europe and America. After the turn
of the century British engineers built the well-known arch bridge
below Victoria Falls, which was intended to form a link in Cecil
Rhodes's Cape-to-Cairo railway. Then came a major advance in
span and load-carrying capacity with Lindenthal's Hell Gate
bridge opened in New York in 1916. This bridge carried four railway tracks and is by far the most heavily loaded long-span bridge
in the world. Moreover, it proved to be the forerunner of the
famous Sydney Harbour bridge, which is the biggest arch yet built.

In Portugal are the famous Pia Maria and Luiz I bridges over
the Douro at Oporto, which were completed in 1877 and 1885
respectively. The first of these was the work of two famous French
engineers, Gustave Eiffel, better known as the designer of the
Eiffel Tower, and T. Seyrig, who worked in collaboration with
him from 1868 to 1879. The second bridge was designed by Seyrig.
The Pia Maria bridge is a crescent-shaped iron arch that carries
a single track railway at a height of 250 feet above the river. Like
the St Louis bridge it was erected as two cantilevers without any
falsework. The Luiz I bridge is a tied arch of 566-foot span. It is
a double-decked bridge; the upper roadway runs over the top of
the arch and the lower one is suspended at the level of the springings and incorporates the tie.

In the same year as Seyrig designed the Luiz I bridge, Eiffel
built the graceful Garabit viaduct over the Truyère in the South of
France. Some authorities[1] attribute this bridge to Seyrig, but no

[1] *Encyclopaedia Britannica*, 11th Edition, 1911, and *History of Bridge Engineering*,
H. G. Tyrell, 1911.

mention of him is made in Eiffel's account of the work[1], nor is there any reference to him in the relevant archives of Anciens Etablissements Eiffel. The arch of the Garabit viaduct is similar in shape to that at Pia Maria but of greater span (540 feet) and higher; it carries a single-track railway at a height of more than 400 feet above the gorge. Apart from a short length at each end, it was erected as two cantilevers built out from opposite sides of the valley and tied back to the adjoining spans. A temporary wooden bridge was built beneath it to assist during erection. A novel feature of the bridge is that the railway track was constructed at a level slightly below the top of the supporting ironwork, so that if a train were derailed it would be prevented from toppling off the span. On all these bridges the arch ribs are of wrought-iron and are designed on a batter, i.e. inclined from the vertical, as in the Forth bridge, so that they are wider apart at the bottom than at the top. This practice was adopted to increase stability but was later found to be unnecessary; it complicates the fabrication of the metalwork, increases the cost, and was discontinued about 1910; since then bridge trusses have generally been made vertical.

Before the end of the century two more fine arch bridges were built in Germany. These were the sturdy Kaiser-Wilhelm bridge at Müngsten (1897) and the Dusseldorf bridge over the Rhine (1898). The Kaiser-Wilhelm bridge was designed by A. Rieppel and had a span of 557 feet between centres of towers. Temporary workshops were built at the site and the erection of the bridge, which occupied nearly two years and was carried out by the cantilever method, proved very costly. The bridge at Dusseldorf carried a roadway 46 feet wide and had a span of 595 feet. Both these bridges were destroyed during the second world war.

Two other notable railway arch bridges in France are the masterly Viaur viaduct in Aveyron in the south (1898), and the Austerlitz bridge in Paris (1905). The Viaur viaduct has a central span of 721 feet and a cantilever span at each end of 311 feet. Although somewhat flexible on account of its slender proportions, the bridge perfectly fits its setting. The curved chords of the end cantilevers closely follow and accentuate the upper slopes of the gorge. The Viaur viaduct is further noteworthy as being the first big bridge in France to be built of steel.

*   *   *

[1] *Notice sur le Viaduc de Garabit*, G. Eiffel, Paris 1888.

In 1897 the new Niagara-Clifton arch with braced parallel chords and a span of 840 feet was completed below Niagara Falls. It was the longest arch span of the day and in January 1898 was put to a severe and most unusual test. There was an exceptionally hard winter and, driven by strong westerly winds, great quantities of ice came over the Falls from Lake Erie, so much so that it formed a solid ice barrier, jammed across from shore to shore, three-quarters of a mile above the bridge. Within a short time the river level above the ice dam had risen twenty-five feet and water began to pour over the top of the barrier. Then, with a splintering roar, the great ice dam gave way and the whole mass surged down upon the bridge. The ice piled up over the abutments and was shaved off by the steel ribs of the arch as though by a huge knife. The bridge quivered under the shock, but it stood its ground. Only a few relatively unimportant bracing members were damaged; the main ribs and abutments were uninjured. Subsequently a concrete wall was built around the abutments in an attempt to ward off any recurrence of the peril. Finally, however, in 1938, after the bridge had given forty years' service, the ice had its way and a huge jam wrecked the steelwork at the ends of the ribs.

Within four years another arch, the Rainbow bridge, with a box girder rib of high-tensile steel, 12 feet deep, was built. This bridge, which was designed by Shortridge Hardesty, has a span of 950 feet and a clean simplicity of line which suits the grandeur of its environment (Pl. 26). It is the longest fixed-ended arch in the world and proved to be more rigid and economical than a two-hinged rib would have been. It had been hoped to build it earlier to celebrate the centenary of the Treaty of Ghent, representing one hundred years of peace between Canada and the U.S.A. All workmen on the bridge had to be residents of the country where the work was being done. During its erection twenty-five safety nets were used, some of them from the Golden Gate bridge. Made of manila rope woven into 6-inch squares these nets saved four lives; thanks to them, the bridge was completed without a single serious accident.

*   *   *

Cecil Rhodes's dream of a Cape-to-Cairo railway may never now be realized; there is still a great gap in the heart of Africa stretching from the Congo to the Sudan. But it says much for his drive and power that before his death in 1902, the line stretched 1,500 miles north from Cape Town to the Zambesi. Moreover, the plan he had conceived of a bridge across the gorge of the Zambesi below Victoria Falls was being made into reality.

At the Falls, the brimming mile-wide river suddenly drops sheer down into a gorge that cuts squarely across from bank to bank and is 400 feet deep. Dr Livingstone, who discovered and named the Falls in 1855, reported that they were called by the natives 'Mosi-oa-tunya' which may be translated as 'The Smoke that Thunders'. The noise of the waters can be heard as a distant roaring five or six miles away, and the spray rising in a white cloud high over the gorge looks like smoke from a bush fire. For more than twenty miles below the Falls the river is hemmed in the narrow gorge until it emerges level with the surrounding land.

Rhodes said that he wanted the bridge built where it would be wet by the spray from the Falls—an idea more inspired by his romantic spirit than in conformity with good anti-corrosion practice! Before the bridge was built, the usual crossing was by dugout canoe at the Old Drift, five miles above the Falls. Here, as the railway approached, dwelt a small European settlement. The ground was swampy in the rainy season and the toll taken by blackwater fever and malaria was appalling. In the first winter eleven of thirty-three settlers died; by the end of the next wet season not more than ten of the remainder survived. Anti-malarial and other measures have changed that, and to-day the Victoria Falls and its hotel are a famous holiday resort.

The bridge is a steel arch, but flat-topped and spandrel-braced, and originally had two railway tracks running over the top of it. The foundations were cut out of the rock on the sides of the gorge. The span is 500 feet and the two halves of the arch were built out simultaneously from either side, tied back by temporary cables anchored into the rock, until they met and were joined in the middle. During its construction a Blondin cableway was slung across the gorge and safety nets were suspended beneath the steelwork. It is reported, however, that the steel erectors asked for the nets to be taken away as they made them feel nervous! Some twenty-five years later road traffic had developed to such an extent that the deck of the bridge was modified and a roadway and footpath added to it in place of one of the railway tracks. This necessitated strengthening a number of the lower girders by means of additional steel plates riveted onto the side webs.

The bridge was designed by Sir Ralph Freeman, of whom we shall speak again, under the direction of G. A. Hobson and built by the Cleveland Bridge Co. of Darlington. It was the first of the outstanding steel arches designed by Freeman; the two other best known of his works being the Sydney Harbour bridge in Australia (1924-32) and the Birchenough bridge in Southern Rhodesia (1933-5).

* * *

Now came a major advance in America with the construction of the Hell Gate bridge, of 977-foot span, over the East River in New York. This was the masterpiece of Gustav Lindenthal, who was born in Austria and emigrated when a young man to the United States. An alternative design of a suspension bridge with braced eyebar chains was prepared, but the arch proved to be more rigid and more economical. The foundation on Wards Island presented unusual difficulties. Twenty-one caissons had to be sunk to depths varying from 37 to 107 feet in order to reach rock capable of resisting the thrust from the arch. However, when the ground was excavated it was found that there was a crevasse in the rock from 15 to 60 feet wide of unknown depth, filled with red clay and boulders. To bridge this chasm a concrete arch had to be built below the level of the cutting edge of the caissons, the whole of the work being carried out under compressed air and at considerable risk at a depth of 70 feet below the river.

The superstructure of the bridge consists of a two-hinged spandrel-braced arch of high carbon steel. The bracing is of the usual N-type, which simplifies erection. The ends of the upper chord are given a slight upward reverse curve, which increases the height of the spandrel, or shoulder. This form may be a little puzzling at first, as no doubt the most satisfying form of arch to the layman is the crescent-shape, which is so clearly functional and in which the stress flows obviously to the springings or bearings. To the engineer, the spandrel-braced arch is equally satisfying, as he can appreciate the value of the high shoulder in aiding rigidity and assisting in erection. The two halves of the arch were erected as cantilevers, supported, until they joined, by means of backstays temporarily weighted down. The erection cranes, which travelled out along the upper chords, weighed 315 tons each and were capable of lifting the heaviest pieces of the lower chord, which weighed 180 tons. After the arch had been completed the deck was suspended below it and the bridge opened to traffic in 1916. For sixteen years it was the longest arch span in the world, and is still by far the most heavily loaded long-span bridge.

* * *

Proposals for a bridge or tunnel across Sydney Harbour were made as long ago as 1815, one of the first designs for a bridge being prepared in 1857 by an engineer who had served his time with Robert Stephenson. In 1912 it was decided to build a bridge in preference to a tunnel, and finally, in 1923, the Government of New South Wales called for tenders. Six of the leading bridge-building firms of the world responded. Among them were Dorman, Long and Company who had previously erected no great bridges abroad but were one of the biggest steel producers in England and thoroughly experienced in the fabrication of heavy bridgework; other tenders were submitted by firms in America and Europe. Every known form of bridge suitable for long spans, including combinations of arch, cantilever, and suspension bridges was considered, and the estimates ranged from less than four to more than ten million pounds. One of the seven designs submitted by Dorman Long was selected; this was for an arch bridge with tall granite pylons at the ends, and the contract was let to them in March 1924 for the sum of £4,218,000.

Apart from the curious cross-braced centre panel in the Hell Gate bridge, the outline of the arch spanning Sydney Harbour is very similar to its forerunner. In the Sydney Harbour bridge the pylons at each end are kept well back from the top of the arch, in order to emphasize the fact that the whole of the thrust is transmitted to the ground through the bearings at the ends of the lower chord. In the Hell Gate bridge the reverse procedure was adopted. The pylons were set close up and the ends of the upper chords were actually extended by means of dummy members into the pylons, making it appear as if the upper chord too exerted a thrust. This illustrates the modern preference for functional design, where permissible, as against masking the outline of a bridge to further a fictitious presentation of the way the stress flows.

There is little doubt that Sydney Harbour bridge gripped the imagination of the country because it was the first long-span bridge to be built by British engineers for a generation. It carries four inter-urban railway tracks, a 57-foot wide roadway, and two footpaths. The span of the steel arch is 1,650 feet, and the roadway is suspended below it at a height of 172 feet above the water. Approach spans at either end with a gradient of 1 in 40 lead the traffic onto and off the bridge.

The design was made under the direction of the late Sir Ralph Freeman, the famous consulting engineer of London, who was knighted in 1945 for the work which he had done in the planning and construction of this and other bridges. The erection at site was in charge of Lawrence Ennis, a director of Messrs Dorman, Long & Co. and the scheme was promoted by Dr J. J. C. Bradfield, who was at that time chief engineer to the New South Wales Government. The project was on a vast scale. It involved the construction of a steel arch more than half as long again as the previous biggest. It had more than double the weight of steel in it—38,300 tons. And although the design had to be prepared in London and most of the steel made in Middlesbrough, the bridge had to be built on the other side of the world.

After work had started on the Sydney bridge the contract for the new Tyne bridge at Newcastle was let to the same contractors. The Tyne bridge, for which Messrs Mott, Hay, and Anderson were the consulting engineers, was a crescent-shaped arch of 531-foot span; when completed in 1928 it was the heaviest arch bridge in Europe. The design of Sydney bridge was made first, but the contractors used identical temporary steel cables and sockets etc. in the erection of both bridges. Much of the investigation made for the design of Sydney bridge was of service in both contracts.

In order to check the design, small-scale models were made of a number of the girders for testing to destruction. But such was the scale of the project that even these models were 50 feet long or so, capable of resisting a load of hundreds of tons, and there was no testing machine in the world big enough to take them. A new hydraulic testing machine of 1,250-tons capacity had to be specially built at Dorman Long's Britannia Works in Middlesbrough. During tests, when the yield point was passed, the steel angles would begin to buckle; rivet heads would burst off and fly through the air; then, with a shattering roar, the girder would finally collapse whilst the whole building shook under the recoil of the immense forces unleashed in the machine. Information of considerable value to the designer was obtained from these tests.

The steelwork was fabricated in Sydney in new workshops, specially built and equipped at a cost of £300,000, where 800 men were employed. Much of it was of heavier sections than had ever been made before; steel angles measuring 12 inches by 12 inches by 1¼ inch thick; steel plates 8 foot 3 inches wide by 2¼ inches thick; rivets up to 1⅜ inch diameter and 12 inches long. The machine tools had to be of corresponding size. The planer would machine the edge of a plate 66 feet long and 2¼ inches thick; the straightening machine would roll it flat, and the plate shears would crop it. Overhead cranes of 120-ton capacity were installed to handle the girders during fabrication. After completion they were loaded onto a pontoon in a dock at the delivery end of the shop whence they could be floated out to be lifted into position in the bridge.

The granite for the facing of the pylons was quarried at Moruya, 150 miles south of Sydney. Two hundred and forty men worked here for six years getting the stone for the bridge. To accommodate them and their families a small township had to be built, complete with post office, schools, and shops.

While the workshops were being built and the quarry opened excavations were started for approach span and arch foundations. The rock was a variable yellow sandstone with horizontal seams of clay and shale. The thrust on each of the four bearings, or springing points, of the arch amounted to 19,700 tons, acting at a slope of about 45° to the horizontal. In order to remove weak and fissured rock and get down to reliable sandstone capable of resisting such a thrust, excavations 90 feet long, 40 feet wide and 30 to 40 feet deep had to be made in the rock below each bearing. These excavations were then filled with concrete on which the steel bearings of the bridge were subsequently placed and concreted up. Each of the four bearings had two main web plates of high tensile steel $9\frac{1}{2}$ inches thick and 24 feet long that could only be likened to armour plate used in battleships. These webs distributed the thrust from the arch onto steel castings designed to spread it over a wide area of concrete beneath them. In spite of the massive character of the steelwork, however, it was fabricated with the greatest accuracy. The specified limit of error was 1/1,000 inch in the steelwork and only 1/10,000 inch in the connecting bolts. Whilst the bearings were being erected, their position was controlled by jacks capable of adjusting them in any direction. So precisely were they located, that one whole operation of the eight jacks was undertaken to correct an error in setting out of 1/64 inch.

After the bearings were placed, the building of the bridge out over the water was begun. Each half of the arch was built out from either side of the harbour until the two met and were joined in the middle. To secure each half arch during erection it was temporarily anchored back by means of 128 steel wire ropes, each $2\frac{3}{4}$ inches in diameter and about 1,200 feet long. The total length of cable used was 60 miles. These ropes were attached to the ends of the upper chords of the arch, whence they passed down to the ground and round an inclined U-shaped tunnel cut 100 feet deep in the rock. Thus before the half arch could fall, either the steel ropes or their connections would have to break, or the rock above the tunnel would have to be torn out of place (Fig. 24).

The steel members forming the panels of the arch were lifted into place from the water by two creeper cranes, designed for the purpose, each capable of lifting 120 tons. The under-carriages of these cranes ran on bogies on the upper chords of the bridge and were designed so that they could haul themselves up the slope of

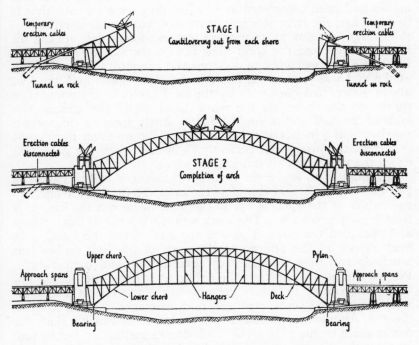

FIG. 24. Diagrammatic views of the erection of Sydney Harbour bridge.

the arch, erecting the steelwork panel by panel in front of them. Each crane weighed 600 tons, and special safety chains were maintained in permanent tension in case of any failure of the hauling gear. For if the crane had been allowed to slip back even an inch, its great weight would have gathered sufficient momentum to carry away all obstacles and so wreck the structure (Pl. 31).

As the two sides were built out towards each other, their ends were repeatedly surveyed in order to check that they were keeping to the correct line and levels. These measurements were made in calm weather at dawn before the heat of the sun was sufficient to affect the steelwork. On the southern half of the arch there was no appreciable error, but the northern half developed a tendency for the end to move to the west. By the time the ninth panel had been reached the east side was 1.1/16 inch too low and the centre line 1⅛ inch to the west of the true position. This slight error was corrected by adjusting the connections of the anchorage cables, and thereafter there was no more trouble. When the two half arches had been completed and before they were joined—that is to say when the structure was in its most vulnerable condition— the bridge was put to its severest test. A violent gale sprang up from the west and the wind blew full on the side of the bridge. Each half arch weighing 14,000 tons and carrying a 600-ton crane at the end was jutting out 800 feet from the shore and 450 feet above water, tied back only by the steel cables to the anchorage tunnel on the shore. As the wind raged round the girders, the ends of the half arches could be seen slowly swaying sideways a maximum of 3 inches one past the other. But no other movement occurred; the bridge felt perfectly rigid and when the gale died down the structure had suffered no harm.

It remained to lower the two halves together and so close the gap between them and complete the arch. To do this the anchorage cables at the ends of the bridge had to be run out one at a time from 3 to 6 inches. The work was carried out in three stages and occupied ten days. Towards the end of the third stage, at four o'clock in the afternoon, the ends of the half arches just touched; and then came a race against time and temperature. For, as the men jacked out the cables as hard as they could go, they were tending to reduce the gap; but as the sun set, the steelwork cooled and contracted and that, of course, tended to open the gap. After sunset the steelwork cooled more quickly than the cables could be run out and the ends drew apart again; but by late evening the men got the upper hand and the two sides of the bridge were finally and permanently joined. Subsequently the upper chord of the arch was completed, and the necessary stress jacked into it to make the arch two-hinged; all the temporary cables were removed (Pl. 32) and the great cranes slowly retreated down the bridge, erecting the hangers and the steelwork of the deck, suspended below the arch. During the construction of the deck one of the erectors fell off the steelwork a distance of 172 feet into the water, a height greater than that of Nelson's column. He was quickly rescued and found to have broken only two ribs. After a week or two in hospital he was back on the job and working undeterred on the deck again.

On completion of the bridge the government engineer collected 72 locomotives weighing 7,600 tons for testing it. These were disposed on the tracks in such a manner as to produce the maximum distortion of the structure. Measurements of the deflection of the arch under these drastic conditions proved slightly less than the calculated figures, so that the strength and sufficiency of the design were demonstrated. On 19 March 1932, almost eight years to a day since the contract was signed, the bridge was opened; British throughout in design, workmanship, and erection, and a lasting tribute to its engineers.

*   *   *

The longest steel arch in America is O. H. Ammann's Bayonne bridge across the Kill van Kull at New York. At the time this bridge was built the ship channel for deep draft vessels was only 400 feet wide, but the War Department requirements included a minimum clear height of 135 feet for the full width of a future 1,000 foot waterway. This and other factors necessitated a minimum river span of 1,500 feet for any type of bridge; and for an arch with haunches below the deck of more than 1,650 feet. As the bridge had to be built as a self-liquidating project numerous alternative types were studied and the adopted arch design proved the most economical.

The unusual site conditions enabled the arch to be supported on temporary trestles during erection. The two sides of it were not joined at mid-span point, but some panels away. It is the only one of the big steel arches that was erected in this way; because the same conditions that necessitate a long span usually preclude any intermediate supports, so that the arch has of necessity to be erected by the cantilever method. The Bayonne bridge is a fine achievement and undoubtedly one of the world's great structures; but, for the reasons stated above, its erection did not present difficulties commensurate with those that had to be overcome at Sydney Harbour.

*   *   *

The most recent long-span arch built by British engineers is the Birchenough bridge in Southern Rhodesia, designed by Sir Ralph Freeman for the Beit Trustees (Pl. 27). The Beit Railway Trust was formed to administer funds bequeathed by Alfred Beit, a close colleague of Cecil Rhodes. These funds were to be used to develop railway and road communications and other public services in Rhodesia. The Birchenough bridge was built to span the Sabi river which in the flood season becomes a torrent more than 1,000 feet wide. The old ford at Moodies Drift is impassable for five months in the year. It is in a most interesting part of the country, not many miles from the railhead at Fort Victoria; this is the oldest town in Rhodesia and was founded by Rhodes's Pioneer Column when they first entered the country in the face of Lobengula's Impis in 1890. The veldt abounds in big game, elephant, rhinoceros, lion, and leopard; herds of bush buck browse amongst the low mopani trees; here and there a baobab tree, hundreds of years old, raises its immense pithy trunk, topped by an insignificant tuft of foliage. Little grey monkeys play amongst the tree tops and baboons drop to the ground to raid the mealie fields.

Nearby are the mysterious Zimbabwe ruins, the scene of Rider Haggard's *King Solomon's Mines* and *Allan Quatermain*. What race built these huge stone cities of the past with their elliptical temples and conical towers will probably never be known. There is not a single inscription to give a clue. But archaeologists say that the character of the buildings is African and it is thought that they may date from between A.D. 500 and 1000 when the country was exploited for gold by Asiatic peoples.

At the site selected for the bridge there were outcrops of rock on both sides of the river; and this, combined with evidence that the sand in the river bed was liable to shift during the floods, indicated an arch bridge as the most economical design. The arch, which has a span of 1,080 feet, is a slender braced parabola of high-tensile steel, from which is suspended a light roadway for two lanes of traffic and a footway. Built at a cost of only £134,600, the bridge marks a definite advance in engineering practice as it is the first bridge of great span to be built for less than the cost of a multi-span bridge.

Two other points of interest to an engineer are that it has no redundant members—not even lateral cross members—and that nearly all the main diagonals are of identical length. It was designed for cantilever erection and a number of the temporary steel cables that had previously been used on the erection of Sydney bridge were employed again on this contract. It is amazing how well they had lasted. In spite of being transported from England to Australia and thence to Africa, and their use on two bridges, they showed no signs of deterioration. In fact under the hot African sun some of the original black grease could be seen oozing out from the inner layers of wire. Subsequently these cables were cut to length and used as permanent hangers for the deck.

On account of the high cost of freight, it was essential to keep the weight of plant and temporary structures to a minimum; 180 tons of steelwork was needed for temporary works but only 40 tons was sent to site for this purpose. The remaining 140 tons were all obtained out of the permanent steelwork of the bridge, by modifying it so that it could be used for both purposes. As an example of the ingenuity exercised, the undercarriages of the creeper cranes were made out of part of the deck bracing and subsequently incorporated in the roadway. Steelwork was transported across the river, to points where it had to be erected in the bridge, by means of a 7-ton electric cableway, or Blondin. Pieces were transferred in mid-air from the cableway to the bridge cranes and so lifted into place.

Owing to the slender proportions of the arch, the effect of wind stresses, particularly during erection, required careful investigation. To this end a number of models of the arch were made and tested in a wind tunnel. This was probably the first occasion on which wind tunnel tests were made on bridge work; but since then the method has been widely adopted, especially of course, for tests on models of suspension bridges.

Chapter 12

THE GREAT SUSPENSION
BRIDGES OF AMERICA

'Bridges of half a mile span, for common or railway
travel, may be built, using iron for the cables, with
entire safety. But by substituting the best quality
of steel wire, we may nearly double the span and
afford the same degree of security.'

JOHN A. ROEBLING, 1855

IT MAY seem like sacrilege to describe the great suspension bridges
of America in a chapter, when ten times that amount of space
might well be devoted to one of them. Nevertheless, in order to
complete our survey and to present the full story to date we must
make the attempt. We shall see how in fifty years the longest span
increased from 1,500 feet to 4,200 feet; how wind forces appeared
to have been mastered but suddenly re-asserted themselves with
catastrophic results; and how the new science of aerodynamics as
related to bridges came urgently into being.

Roebling's prophecy as to the possible spans of the future has
already been borne out. But wire and structural steel are now available of much greater strength than Roebling can have visualized.
There is little doubt that engineers to-day, if the money was provided, could double his forecast and build a single span two miles
long.

*   *   *

Under the stimulus of the successful Brooklyn bridge, it was not
many years before the East River was bridged by two more suspension spans, the Williamsburg bridge completed in 1903 and
Manhattan in 1909. Both these bridges had four main cables of
parallel wires spun in position in the manner invented by Roebling. But the cold-drawn wire used was being steadily improved

in quality, so that its ultimate strength of 71.5 tons per square inch on Brooklyn bridge had been increased to 93.6 on Manhattan. In the calculations for the Manhattan bridge the 'Deflection Theory', by which a substantial saving in the weight of the main cables is achieved, was used for the first time.

Wire cables were steadily superseding links or eyebars, such as had been used by Telford in the Menai bridge and subsequently most effectively by William Tiernay Clark in his famous bridge over the Danube at Budapest. Clark's slender and graceful bridge of 666-foot span, completed in 1849, stood until it was rebuilt, except for the towers and anchorages, in 1914. Some fifty years later it was emulated, though not successfully, by the Elizabeth bridge in Budapest, which though of greater span had short straight backstays and lacked the pleasing proportions of its forerunner. Its method of erection was undistinguished as, instead of supporting the eyebars during assembly by means of temporary cables, slung across the span, a great mass of timber falsework was constructed to carry them. Apart from the expense in time and money this method would be impracticable in wide deep rivers like those, for instance, surrounding New York. Except on very short spans wire rope cables would normally be more economical than links, and it is significant that in none of the long spans built in the last twenty years have eyebars been used.

Another variation that was tried was to stiffen the cable or chain instead of stiffening the deck of the bridge. The Point bridge built at Pittsburgh in 1877 was a notable example of this method. The span of 800 feet had no stiffening truss at deck level but the eyebar chain itself was braced. Examples nearer home are the side spans of the famous Tower bridge[1] in London, a bridge more notable for its place in the hearts of Londoners than for any great technical merit. The Florianopolis bridge in Brazil designed by Steinman and Robinson and erected in 1924-26 was a further interesting variant. In this span of 1,114 feet eyebar chains were found to be more economical than wire cables. The stiffening trusses were built in the usual way in the deck, but incorporated the middle portion of the eyebar chain to form the upper members.

[1] H. Heathcote Statham, R.I.B.A., a contemporary critic wrote in 1899: 'The Tower bridge represents the vice of tawdriness and pretentiousness and of falsification of the actual facts of the structure. . . . The exceedingly heavy suspension chains are made to appear to hang on an ornamental stone structure which they would in reality drag down, and the side walls of the apparently solid tower rest on part of the iron structure and you could see under them before the roadway was made up. All architects would have much preferred the plain steel structure to this kind of sham.' Waddell agrees and adds that it is 'the most monumental example of extravagance in bridge construction in the world.'

This form of construction is well calculated to provide aerodynamic stability[1].

Wire rope cables may be one of three kinds: parallel wires, stranded wire ropes, or locked-coil cables. Cables of parallel wires were invented, as we have seen, by Roebling, and constitute the standard American practice to-day. They will generally be found economical for spans over 1,500 feet, particularly in the United States, where the specialized plant required for their erection is in existence.

Cables of stranded wire ropes were first used in France and have subsequently been employed in all the long-span suspension bridges in Canada. They were used in the Island of Orleans bridge (1935) and the mighty Lion's Gate bridge (1939) at Vancouver. Designed by Messrs Monsarrat and Pratley, Consulting Engineers of Montreal, these bridges have spans of 1,059 and 1,550 feet respectively, and are the longest in the British Empire. The cables of the Island of Orleans bridge are made up of thirty-seven strands of twisted wire having an ultimate strength of 81.5 tons per square inch. The strands had to be tensioned up to more than half their ultimate strength before erection, in order to take out the initial stretch that occurs when the wires first compact together under load, and which may amount to nearly an inch per hundred feet of length. Stranded ropes, of course, cost more initially than galvanized wire; but they can be pulled across the river a strand at a time and the cost of erection would generally be less than for parallel wire cables. A cable made up of stranded ropes is more difficult to protect against corrosion, on account of the interstices between the strands, than is a parallel wire cable, which can be squeezed to a circular section and bound.

Locked coil cables are stranded ropes formed of specially shaped wires that lock together to form a compact round strand. This type was used in the Cologne-Mulheim bridge and also in the new Chelsea bridge over the Thames, designed by Messrs Rendel, Palmer & Tritton and erected in 1934-37.

* * *

A suspension bridge of particular interest on account of the formation of the cables is the Otto Beit bridge that was designed by Sir Ralph Freeman and built in 1938-39 over the Zambesi river. For although the span was little more than 1,000 feet and

---

[1] The Indooroopilly bridge of 600-foot span, built at Brisbane in 1936 out of cables that had been used for the erection of Sydney Harbour bridge, is of this type.

the bridge only carried a light roadway, old problems were treated in an original manner. The cables are of parallel wires arranged in forty layers, or flat ribbons, which were pulled across the span and erected a layer at a time. In almost every case where they had been used before, parallel wire cables had been spun in place by Roebling's method, loops of wire being pulled across on a pulley. Moreover, in the Otto Beit bridge the ends of the wires were cut to length and connected by means of white metal filling into cast-steel sockets, instead of being looped round strand shoes at the anchorages as in American practice.

After the towers and cables had been erected, the deck steel-work was assembled by means of the same cableway, or 'Blondin' that had been used on the Birchenough bridge. This time it was erected over the river on the centre line of the span, and diamond-shaped openings were provided in the tower bracing to allow the cableway and load to pass through. Another innovation of particular interest to designers is the method of attachment of the hangers to the deck. Instead of being connected to the top of the stiffening truss, the hangers are brought down outside it and attached to the ends of the cross girders supporting the roadway. This arrangement not only achieved a saving in height and weight of the towers but also had advantages in erection; for it enabled the cross girders to be erected first, right across the span, after which the remainder of the deck steelwork could be laid in place through-out its length. By this means the distortions which would other-wise have arisen as the stiffening girders were erected from either end were avoided; these distortions are, of course, only temporary, but they add to the difficulties of erection.

* * *

In 1926 the Camden bridge over the Delaware River at Phil-adelphia, designed by Modjeski, Webster, and Ball, was com-pleted. This bridge of 1,750-foot span has two parallel wire cables each 30 inches in diameter. The deck is 128 feet wide and carries inter-urban trains as well as roadway traffic; in addition there are two overhead footways. The footways are cantilevered out on either side of the deck and have the advantage of increasing its aerody-namic stability. Towers of cellular steel construction, subsequently widely adopted, were used for the first time. The experiments on the buckling of steel plates and other tests made in connection with the design of these towers are of considerable value to-day.

* * *

Experiments were continually proceeding in an attempt to produce stronger wire to use in the cables, and with this end in view a new kind of wire, heat-treated instead of cold-drawn, was developed by the American Cable Company. This wire had only slightly greater ultimate strength, but its yield point was 84.8 tons per square inch as against 64.4 for cold-drawn wire. It proved remarkably tough and deformable in severe laboratory tests and it was considered safe to increase its working stress to 37.5 as against 33.9 tons per square inch adopted up to then for cold-drawn wire.

The new heat-treated wire was used in two great bridges on which work began in 1927. These were the Ambassador bridge of 1,850-foot span, making a link in the highway between America and Canada across the Detroit river, and the smaller Mount Hope bridge near Bristol, Rhode Island. In February 1929, when the Mount Hope bridge was nearly completed, some broken wires were found at the point where individual strands of the cable were bent round the strand shoes at the anchorage. A careful investigation was made and it was found that although the stress in the cable was still less than half the final figure, in some of the strands more than three quarters of the wires had broken. Work was at once halted on both bridges. The construction of the Ambassador bridge was not far advanced and the cables had only attained ⅛ of their final stress. Nevertheless, a number of broken wires were discovered. It is to the credit of the contractors that without any hesitation they announced their intention of dismantling the bridges, scrapping the cables, and replacing them with cold-drawn wire.

On the Mount Hope bridge this involved taking down part of the deck steelwork and all of the stiffening trusses and hangers, and caused some six months' delay. Work on the Ambassador bridge, however, was nearly a year ahead of schedule when the breaks were discovered, and even after the cables had been replaced the bridge was still completed and opened some months before the contract date. This experience is of interest, as it shows the limitations of the most comprehensive laboratory tests. It is only by use under working conditions, and even then only after tests lasting a number of years, that engineers can know with certainty the qualities of the materials they use[1].

*   *   *

[1] The U.S. Bureau of Standards reported subsequently that the failure was mainly due to the effect of alternating stresses on the fine-grained structure of the heat-treated wire. The fibrous structure of cold-drawn wire was able to resist such stresses.

The next major advance in size was achieved in the George Washington bridge over the Hudson River (Pl. 37). With lattice-steel towers 595 feet high and a clear span of 3,500 feet this bridge, designed by O. H. Ammann, Chief Engineer of the Port of New York Authority, dwarfed all its predecessors. The roadway, which carries eight lanes of traffic, was suspended from four cables each 36 inches in diameter, built up of 26,474 wires. The total length of wire used was 105,000 miles, sufficient to go four times round the earth. The bridge was designed to carry two decks one above the other. At present only the upper roadway has been constructed but it is intended to built the second deck, which will carry four more lanes of heavy vehicles, as soon as traffic warrants it.

A remarkable feature of this bridge is that it is the only long-span suspension bridge that has no stiffening truss and appears to be quite stable without it. Its weight and inertia are so great compared with the live load, and the cables so massive, that the bridge suffers no undue deflection under either traffic or wind forces. When the second roadway is added it is planned to build stiffening trusses inter-connecting the two decks.

The foundations for the New Jersey pier were built inside two cofferdams which were bigger and deeper than any previously used on bridge construction. The cofferdams were made of steel sheet piling, driven to depths varying from 40 feet inshore to 85 feet along the deepest part of the river face. Here a double wall was used, two lines of sheeting being driven approximately 8 feet apart and the space between filled with concrete at the base and silt higher up. Each cofferdam measured 108 feet by 99 feet in plan. The frames inside them, which had to resist hydrostatic pressure, consisted of steel walings[1] braced across the dam by means of timber struts. When the cofferdams were completed the water inside them was pumped out, enabling the rock to be excavated and the bridge piers built in the dry.

It was originally intended to encase the steel towers in stone-faced concrete. This provision was perhaps wisely omitted, but the closely-braced towers lack the fine appearance of those of the Camden and a few earlier suspension bridges. A feature that may be puzzling at first sight is that the pairs of cables are not placed centrally over each leg of the tower but are over the inner faces; a disposition which may not appear to make the fullest use of the steel in the tower. The reason for this arrangement is to space the legs of the towers as far apart as possible, in order to prevent them

[1] A series of horizontal beams, one below the other, inside the sheet piling.

from obstructing the width of the roadway. It is in fact an example of bold and purposeful design. The outer legs of the towers brace the inner ones and Ammann has shown that at the bottom of the inner and outer legs the stresses are equalized.

Before the spinning of the cables was begun, two temporary foot-bridges had to be erected across the span 3 feet below the position that the main cables would assume. The cold-drawn galvanized wires, each 0.196 inches in diameter, and having a minimum ultimate strength of 98 tons per square inch, which were built up to form the cables, were then spun in place by a method essentially the same as that described on page 91. On account of the enormous amount of wire to be handled, however, the spinning plant was mechanized to a greater extent than on any previous contract; in fact the George Washington bridge may be regarded as the pioneer of modern mechanical methods of cable erection. Preliminary and final squeezing machines were designed to travel along the cables and compress the wires together. The final squeezers consisted of steel rings, or yokes, that encircled the cable and contained twelve hydraulic plungers arranged radially which exerted an enormous pressure on the wires to squeeze them into a compact circular form (Pl. 38). The squeezer was applied at intervals of 2 to 4 feet along the span. The last operation on the cables, which was not carried out until after the deck had been erected, and when the cables had taken up their full stretch, was to bind them tightly round with a continuous wire wrapping between the cable bands. This was done by means of electrically-operated wrapping machines, which encircled the cable and travelled slowly along it. As it is driven along, this machine rotates and wraps a galvanized wire tightly round the compacted cable, the ends of the wire being secured against the sides of the cable bands.

After the vertical hangers had been suspended from the cable bands, the steelwork of the deck was built outwards from the towers. This was done by means of four travelling derricks which moved out along the deck erecting the steelwork panel by panel in front of them. The heaviest lifts were 62 tons.

Work at site started in September 1927 and the bridge was opened in October 1931. Financed by the Port of New York Authority, it cost 75 million dollars and carries five million vehicles per annum. The George Washington bridge is by no means the only great work for which its distinguished designer, Ammann, has been responsible. In his early days he played an important part in the construction of the Hell Gate bridge and the Lincoln tunnel below the Hudson river. Subsequently he designed the Bayonne, Triborough, and Bronx-Whitestone bridges in New York. In addition Ammann advised on the construction of the Golden Gate bridge and served on the commission of enquiry into the strength of Brooklyn bridge and the failure of Tacoma Narrows.

* * *

And now we must turn to San Francisco, the 'City by the Golden Gate', on the other side of the continent. It was here that the terrible earthquake and fire occurred in 1906, when nearly a thousand persons lost their lives and the damage to property is said to have amounted to 100 million pounds. Yet the fact that San Francisco Bay is located in the heart of the earthquake belt has not deterred engineers from building two of the world's greatest bridges there in the last twenty years. And one of them, the longest single span in the world, is sited within six miles of the line of action of the 1906 earthquake. What clearer proof could the designers give of their confidence in the earthquake-proof construction of to-day?

It is not imagined, of course, that any bridge could withstand an earthquake of catastrophic force in close proximity. But engineers believe that a suitably designed bridge should be capable of surviving earthquakes of intensity up to Grade 8 on the Rossi-Forel[1] scale. To do this they must be well braced, securely anchored, and have plenty of room for movement at the expansion joints; and they must be designed to resist a horizontal force equal to one tenth of the weight of the bridge acting in any direction.

The city of San Francisco lies at the north end of a long spit of land on the west side of the bay. It was cut off from the Marin County to the north by the Golden Gate Strait, so-called because ships passing out of the bay into the Pacific in the evening sailed straight into the rays of the setting sun. And it was separated from the hinterland to the east by the width of the bay. In 1933 work commenced under the direction of the late C. H. Purcell, the chief engineer, on the construction of the Bay bridge to connect the city with the mainland to the east via Yerba Buena Island; the crystallization of a project which had been discussed since the pioneer days of 1868. The crossing, which is 4¼ miles long, con-

---

[1] Earthquakes are graded from 1 to 10 in accordance with a standard scale of intensity devised by Messrs Rossi and Forel. In Grade 8 large cracks may appear in the ground and ordinary houses be damaged beyond repair.

sists of twin suspension bridges each of 2,310-foot span with a common central anchorage; a tunnel 540 feet long through the island; and a cantilever bridge of 1,400-foot span with approaches on the eastern side. The bridge is double-decked and carries six lanes of light traffic on the upper deck and three lanes of heavy vehicles and two inter-urban tracks below.

The foundations presented extraordinary difficulties. They required caissons of unprecedented size to be sunk through deep water, in a current of $7\frac{1}{2}$ knots, and to a depth beyond that at which men can work under compressed air. The biggest caisson was that for the central anchorage (Pl. 34). This measured 197 feet by 92 feet in plan and was built up of fifty-five vertical steel cylinders. It had to be constructed on a slipway, launched, towed to site, anchored, and then sunk to a depth of more than 200 feet onto an irregular and sloping surface of rock. Each cylinder was sealed by means of a steel dome which was welded on top of it. Compressed air was used inside the cylinders to give the caisson buoyancy and to control the sinking. The domes were cut off the tops of groups of cylinders in turn to enable the muck to be grabbed out through them from the bed of the bay. To increase the height of the cylinders as the caisson was sunk, new steel lengths were welded on and the domes re-welded on top again. In the early stages of sinking the huge caisson rocked from side to side, plunging down and heaving up the subsoil around it, until the material encountered had sufficient strength to support its weight. When the surface of the rock was reached it was shattered by means of a 5-ton 'gad', a long pointed steel weight, which was dropped onto it down the cylinders; the broken rock was cleared from beneath the cutting edges by divers and grabbed to the surface. By this means the rock was levelled so that the caisson could be founded on a horizontal rock bed. After inspection and cleaning up, the middle twenty-five cylinders were sealed with concrete deposited under water. Subsequently the remaining cylinders were concreted and the foundation completed.

We have no space to describe in detail the building of the superstructure; how the steel towers were erected by climbing hammer-headed cranes, the temporary footbridges slung across the span, the main cables erected by double-sheaved spinning wheels that made mile-long trips high above the bay and placed 128 tons of wire per day (Pl. 33); how the cable strands were connected to the anchorages, the completed cables compacted and bound, and how the hangers were erected and the steelwork of the deck and stiffening trusses assembled. A novel method was used in the erection of the deck. Units of deck and stiffening truss weighing up to 204 tons were erected in the yard, floated out, and lifted into position by light travelling cranes. The tackle was suspended immediately below the cables and the lead lines extended to the base of the towers where the hoisting engines were located (Pl. 35). Erection was begun at the centre of the main span and the ends of the side spans. After the deck had been riveted, the roadway concreted, and the tracks laid, the bridge was opened to traffic in November 1936 (Pl. 36).

* * *

In the same year as this bridge was commenced, work began on another great bridge in San Francisco Bay to span the Golden Gate itself (Pl. 42). Needless to say the project had a long historical background. The assent of the War Department was obtained (in 1923) only because there was sufficient depth of water for the bridge to sink, if it were wrecked, without causing any obstruction to shipping. Finally in 1930 a design was made for a suspension bridge with a main span of 4,200 feet (four-fifths of a mile). The work was under the direction of the late J. B. Strauss, the chief engineer. With a deck 90 feet wide suspended from two cables 36 inches in diameter, the bridge was in all except load-carrying capacity, the largest single span in the world. As we have seen a bridge can hold this proud title only for a brief time; plans are already being discussed for no fewer than three bridges that would surpass it. One of these is for a bridge across the lower reaches of New York Harbour; another is a project prepared at the request of the Italian Government for a 5,000-foot span across the Straits of Messina; and the third is a design made by a famous British engineer for a suspension bridge across the Humber.

The construction of the Golden Gate bridge presented unique difficulties, particularly in the building of the foundations, which had to be made on the ocean bed. The north pier was founded on rock in 20 feet of water at the foot of a cliff. It was built inside a timber framework weighed down by broken rock and surrounded by steel sheet piles. The work was difficult because the bay is tidal and the waters sweep in and out of the entrance four times in every twenty-four hours, reaching a velocity of $7\frac{1}{2}$ knots; there are only four periods of twenty minutes each at the turn of the tide when there is reasonably slack water. These conditions, however, really made themselves felt when work on the foundation of the south pier began. Much of this was underwater work that could only be done by deep-sea divers during the short periods of slack water. At any other time the divers would be swept away by the tide. The south pier is located in deep water virtually in the open sea, 1,125 feet from the shore, and was built inside a huge elliptical fender, or 'bath-tub' as it was called by the workmen (Pl. 43). The fender measured 300 feet by 155 feet and is founded on bedrock 100 feet below water level. The first operation was to construct an access trestle leading out from the shore to the site of the pier. This was no easy job, as the piles supporting it had to be driven down into solid rock by blasting. Nor was its life long, for no sooner had it been completed than a freight steamer crashed through it in a fog, carrying away 300 feet in the middle. When this had been replaced a great storm blew up and wrecked 800 feet of the trestle, including the 50-ton steel guide frame at the end of it which had been weakened by the previous collision.

An average thickness of 15 feet of serpentine rock had to be excavated over the whole area of the fender at a minimum depth of 65 feet below water; and a novel method of underwater blasting was evolved. Small holes were first drilled 2 feet deep in the rock through a pipe lowered from a floating craft. By means of a number of small bombs, successively inserted and detonated, these holes were enlarged to a depth of 18 feet or so. Six large bombs 8 inches in diameter and 20 feet long were then rammed into adjacent holes and detonated simultaneously. By this means a big volume of rock was shattered and dredged up, and ultimately the necessary excavation was achieved over the whole area. Work on the construction of the fender was then begun. It was built in twenty-two sections each 33 feet long, the first unit being at the end of the access trestle. Concrete was poured below water into steel box shutters held in place by the guide frame at the end of the trestle. After the first section had been concreted to its final height of 15 feet above water, other sections were built out from either side of it; ultimately all twenty-two sections were completed, the fender ring was closed, and the bottom of it sealed with 36 foot depth of concrete placed under water. The top level of eight sections at the east end, however, was kept 40 feet below water level, as the next operation was to float in a steel caisson in which the pier was to be built.

The caisson, measuring 90 feet by 180 feet and weighing 8,000 tons, was towed to site on 9 October 1934, and manoeuvred into place inside the fender. In spite of its great weight, however, it was tossed about by a long ground swell out of the Pacific and battered against the concrete wall. It would take a fortnight at least to complete the gap in the fender wall where the caisson had been floated in, and the engineers had to consider the risk of the caisson being wrecked in the event of a storm arising in that period. An immediate decision had to be reached, and they made up their minds at once. Without delay the caisson was towed out again for scrapping[1] and another scheme was put into operation. Instead of building the pier inside the caisson they now proposed to complete the fender ring and place a further 29 feet of concrete inside it under water, making the total depth of concrete 65 feet. It would then be safe to pump out the water inside the 'bath-tub', so that they would have a dry concrete foundation surrounded by the fender wall in which to build the pier of the bridge. Virtually they switched from a caisson to a cofferdam and proved their resource by rising to the challenge of the sea and changing their plans so as to turn what might have been disaster into success.

The steel towers of the bridge, which are 746 feet high, have legs of cellular design, as first developed in the Camden bridge, with only horizontal bracing between them above the roadway. At the base, each leg is built up of ninety-seven cells 3 foot 6 inches square, constructed of vertical steel plates $\frac{7}{8}$ inch thick. As the height increases the tower is tapered by successively reducing the number of cells until, at the top, just below the cable saddle, there are only twenty-one. The legs of the towers were erected in 45-foot sections by means of electric derricks that were hoisted up stage by stage between them.

The cables were spun by the methods developed on the George Washington bridge, but with even more refinements. Eight sets of hauling ropes and spinning wheels were used, driven by electric motors, and the loops of wire were moved from one wheel to another at mid-span. The tension in the wires was automatically equalized by means of floating counterweights and an increase of 60% in the speed of stringing attained. After the hangers had been assembled, the deck was erected by means of light cranes which moved out along it working from the towers and erecting the steelwork panel by panel in front of them. By the beginning of 1937 the steelwork had all been assembled and the concreting of the deck begun. And then, in spite of all the precautions that had been taken, there was a tragic accident resulting in the death of ten men. An aluminium castor holding a scaffold below the deck broke; the scaffold fell, crashed through the safety net suspended below it, and plunged into the water 240 feet below. It is a sad

---

[1] After various misadventures the caisson was finally sunk in the Pacific 30 miles offshore.

reflection that no means has yet been found of preventing big bridges, like all other great structures, from exacting their toll in human lives.

The bridge was finally opened to traffic in May, 1937, only six months after the Bay bridge. It had cost some 35 million dollars, whereas the Bay bridge had cost 61 million. And that brings us to the question, how are these great bridges financed? The combined cost of the two bridges was 96 million dollars, nearly £20,000,000 at the rate of exchange when they were built, an enormous sum for one city, even as great as San Francisco, to afford. The answer is that tolls are charged on all traffic using the bridges. The money needed to build the bridge is usually raised by selling bonds of the Toll Bridge Authority to private financial interests. In the case of the Golden Gate bridge, the capital was guaranteed by the income from the tolls and the value of property in the city. The bonds were to be redeemed in forty years by means of the income from the tolls, and then the State might take over and the bridge become free.

When the Bay bridge was being promoted, the state of the market caused by the financial depression of 1930 made the customary method of raising money impossible. But after carefully investigating the scheme, the Reconstruction Finance Corporation agreed in 1932 to buy bonds to the value of 61 million dollars to pay for the construction of the bridge, as they were satisfied that it was a sound self-liquidating project. Their confidence was justified, as the cross-bay traffic was trebled within three years of the bridge being opened, and there is no doubt whatever that the income from the tolls will be more than sufficient to pay off the first cost of the bridge, together with its upkeep and the interest on the money, in the course of a few years. In fact the volume of traffic is now so great that not only has the scale of toll charges been reduced, but there is an insistent demand for another bridge!

It is true that the collection of tolls on bridges is a nuisance; but it is much less inconvenient than having to use a ferry; and, if well organized, causes no appreciable delay to traffic. Experience in America shows that a toll booth can serve about 350 vehicles per hour, so that if two booths are provided per traffic lane, cars can be passed at the rate of one every five seconds per lane. Sydney Harbour bridge also operates on the toll system and most successfully. Since it was opened the volume of traffic has increased from one million to fifteen million vehicles per annum. And although the toll charged is only 6d. per car and 3d. per occupant, the bridge showed a net operational surplus by 1952 of £400.000.

In Britain new toll bridges are not permitted, and the money for construction has to be found by the Ministry of Transport with help from local authorities. Unfortunately this method does not result in new bridges being built, or at any rate it seriously delays them. No long-span road bridge has yet been built in Britain, although they have been badly needed for years past, and designs have been prepared for bridges across the lower reaches of the Severn, the Forth, and the Humber, to mention only a few of our wide river estuaries. Moreover, experience has shown time and again that a properly situated new bridge creates traffic and thus acts as a spur and stimulus to industry. Let us hope that these bridges may soon be built, whether they are to be toll or free. For there is no doubt whatever which is preferable, if the alternatives are a toll bridge or no bridge at all!

*   *   *

As we have already seen, Roebling mastered the problem of providing adequate wind stays and stiffening trusses in the Brooklyn bridge. For some fifty years thereafter there was little trouble from wind forces on big bridges, and, as confidence grew, spans were increased, widths of deck narrowed, and depths of stiffening trusses reduced. Particulars of this trend can be seen in Table II. The huge George Washington bridge proved perfectly stable without any stiffening truss whatever, but it was a wide, heavy structure. The width of the Ambassador bridge was only 59 feet 6 inches and of the Bay bridge 66 feet but they both had deep stiffening trusses. The Golden Gate bridge was a notable advance in slenderness, the ratio of span to width being 4200:90 and the stiffening trusses only 25 feet deep. It was estimated that in a gale of 120 m.p.h. the mid-span point of the deck would sway 21 feet either side, but this was not considered objectionable.

Then in 1939 and 1940 two most beautiful and graceful bridges were completed; the Bronx-Whitestone bridge designed by Ammann, and the Tacoma Narrows bridge designed by Moisseiff. The first of these had a span: width ratio of 2,300:74 and the second 2,800:39. Not a great deal of traffic could be anticipated at first on the Tacoma Narrows bridge; therefore a wide roadway was not required. Moreover, economy was essential as the tolls could not be expected to bring in very much income. In both bridges the deck was stiffened by plate girders instead of trusses, the depths being only 11 feet and 8 feet respectively. Thus not only were the bridges less resistant to wind in that they were more

Table II.—PARTICULARS OF SOME OF THE MOST FAMOUS AMERICAN SUSPENSION BRIDGES

Name	Location	Date of Completion	Centre Span ft.	Width between Cables ft.	Depth of Stiffening Truss ft.	Ratio Width to Span	Ratio Depth to Span	Number of Cables	Diameter of Cables inches
Brooklyn	New York N.Y.	1883	1,595	85	17 & 8'-9"	1 : 19	1 : 94	4	15¼
Williamsburg	New York N.Y.	1903	1,600	67	40	1 : 24	1 : 40	4	18¾
Manhattan	New York N.Y.	1909	1,470	96	24	1 : 14	1 : 68	2	20¾
Camden	Philadelphia, Pa.	1921	1,750	89	28	1 : 20	1 : 62	2	30
Ambassador	Detroit, Mich.	1929	1,850	59.5	22	1 : 31	1 : 84	2	19¼
Geo. Washington	New York N.Y.	1931	3,500	106	None	1 : 33	—	4	36
Bay Bridge	San Francisco	1936	2,310	66	30	1 : 33	1 : 85	2	28⅝
Golden Gate	San Francisco	1937	4,200	90	25	1 : 47	1 : 168	2	36¼
Bronx-Whitestone	New York N.Y.	1939	2,300	74	11	1 : 31	1 : 209	2	22
Tacoma Narrows (1st)	Tacoma Wash.	1940	2,800	39	8	1 : 72	1 : 350	2	17¼
Tacoma Narrows (2nd)	Tacoma, Wash.	1950	2,800	60	33	1 : 47	1 : 85	2	20

slender, particularly the Tacoma Narrows bridge, than any previous long-span bridge, but the force of the wind on them would
be proportionately greater, owing to the area presented by the
solid plate girders in the deck being larger than that of the usual
latticed stiffening trusses. The point must be stressed, however,
that both bridges had been most efficiently designed according to
the usual exacting specification, and appeared amply sufficient
to withstand all the customary forces and loads including the
usual allowance for aerostatic forces on the roadway.

The Tacoma Narrows bridge, which was the third longest
span in the world, was opened to traffic on 1 July 1940 and, owing
to its behaviour in wind, was promptly nicknamed 'Galloping
Gertie' (Pl. 40). Not only did the deck sway sideways but appreciable vertical waves appeared, and the roadway oscillated up
and down alarmingly under the action of quite moderate winds.
Drivers of cars reported that vehicles ahead of them completely
disappeared from view and reappeared several times, owing to
the undulations of the roadway, as they crossed the bridge.
Before it was opened, hydraulic buffers had been installed between the ends of the deck and the towers; and an attempt had
been made by means of diagonal ties to reduce movements between the deck and the cables at mid-span. Three months later
a further attempt was made to damp out the oscillations of the
main span by tying down the side spans by means of cables fixed
to concrete blocks in the ground. But it was all to no avail. On
7 November 1940, only four months after the bridge was completed, it collapsed under the action of a wind of only 42 m.p.h.
(Pl. 39). Bridges are designed to withstand gales of 120 m.p.h. and
as the wind pressure varies according to the square of its velocity,
the wind force would only have been about one ninth of the
design pressure.

The storm which had been blowing up overnight reached this
velocity by nine o'clock in the morning. By that time the deck of
the bridge was heaving up and down in waves thirty feet high and
twisting around through an angle of nearly 45° to either side. A
car trapped on the road was sliding about under the movements
of the bridge, and was uncontrollable. Then, suddenly, just before
11 o'clock, a number of the hangers connecting the deck to the
cables snapped in succession and flew high in the air; a thousand
foot length of the deck crashed into the water. The violent twisting
motion then ceased, and the bridge appeared to steady itself; but
quickly the movements were renewed and transmitted to the side
spans; at once nearly the whole of the remainder of the deck of

the main span collapsed; the side spans then sank down, slowly lost their motion, and the wreck of the bridge became practically still.

The collapse of the Tacoma Narrows bridge, after fifty years of immunity from failures of this kind, came as a severe shock to the whole engineering profession. Why should a great span, more than half a mile in length, built of steel and concrete and weighing tens of thousands of tons, become alive, and undulate under quite light wind forces? And why should a slow, steady, comparatively harmless motion suddenly become transformed into a fierce catastrophic frenzy that tears the bridge to pieces? To answer these questions the new science of aerodynamics as applied to bridges has come sharply to the fore. The phenomenon is analogous to the flapping of a long pennant streaming out in the wind or the occurrence of 'wing flutter' in aircraft.

An immense amount of work is being done by means of tests on models of bridges in wind tunnels and analysis of the effect of wind on various shapes of structures. For the Tacoma Narrows is by no means the only suspension bridge in which motions of this kind have been observed. Small movements were noticeable to persons crossing the Bronx-Whitestone bridge; several not wholly satisfactory attempts were made to damp out the motion, and in 1946 the drastic but successful step was taken of building deep stiffening trusses in the deck above the existing girders. In addition to this, diagonal wind stays have been built from the tops of the towers to the deck, similar to those used in the Brooklyn bridge.

Even the mighty Golden Gate bridge has not been completely immune. In 1938 and again in 1941 under a wind velocity of 62 m.p.h. a succession of waves or ripples 2 feet high was observed to run along the deck. On both these occasions, however, the wind was from an unusual quarter and blowing at 45° to the axis of the bridge. Motion-recording instruments were installed, and in December 1951 during a four-hour gale that reached an intensity of 69 m.p.h., vertical movements up to 130 inches were measured in the deck, which was swinging 12 feet sideways in either direction. Some 70,000 dollars worth of damage was suffered by the bridge which was closed by traffic patrols for three hours. Two smaller modern bridges on which undesirable movements have been set up by wind are the Thousand Islands bridge between the U.S.A. and Canada and the Deer Isle bridge in Maine. Both these bridges are stiffened by shallow plate girders. The Golden Gate bridge appears to be the only one with latticed stiffening trusses on which vertical movements due to wind have been observed.

Dr D. B. Steinman, who has taken a prominent part in aerodynamic investigation in America, has calculated the 'coefficient of rigidity' for the biggest suspension bridges. As a result, he finds that all the plate-girder suspension bridges in which this coefficient is less than 15, and all the open-truss suspension bridges in which it is less than 6, have been subject to undesirable aerodynamic oscillations. It appears that winds blowing slightly upwards under the deck of a bridge are liable to have most effect. Methods of combating the wind effect are based on setting up eddies or turbulence in the wind and increasing the rigidity of the structure.

To achieve the first object one or more slots may be left open along the length of the roadway, the height of the parapet may be varied, and cantilevered footways may be built to act as horizontal fins and so prevent the wind from building up a rhythmic oscillation in the bridge. Under the second heading, the weight, depth, and width of the bridge may be increased, longitudinal diagonal stays may be fixed between the cable and the deck to reduce movements of one relative to the other, and artificial damping devices may be introduced.

Such are the lines along which engineers are working to-day, both on models in wind tunnels and on bridges in the field. For the design of the proposed new Severn bridge, a suspension bridge of 3,300-foot span, a 55-foot long model has been made on which exhaustive tests have been carried out in a wind tunnel belonging to the National Physical Laboratory, Teddington. The results of these tests will be of great value to the designers of future long-span bridges.

The Washington Toll Bridge Authority started the reconstruction of the Tacoma Narrows bridge in 1949. The original piers and approaches and part of the anchorages were retained, but the width of the bridge was increased from 39 to 60 feet; it now carries four traffic lanes, and stiffening trusses 33 feet deep have been provided. These trusses are four times as deep as the previous girders and have thirty-seven times the stiffness. Moreover, the bridge is now considerably heavier than before and a number of open slots have been left in the roadway between the traffic lanes to reduce the effect of the wind. Opened to traffic in October 1950, the bridge marks the latest phase in the age-long war between engineers and the forces of nature (Pl. 41).

Bibliography

The principal sources consulted in preparing this book are given below. Original accounts have been used where possible but general histories of bridges have provided a valuable check. For bridges built during the last eighty years the leading technical journals have also been consulted.

AMMANN, O. H., 'Hell Gate Arch Bridge', *Trans. Am. Soc. C.E.*, Vol. LXXXII.

ANONYMOUS, *Charte Avignonnaise des Actes de Saint Bénézet*, 1230-60.

BAKER, BENJAMIN, *Long-Span Railway Bridges*, 1867.

BATESON, E. *See* WARD, A. M.,

BILL, MAX, *Robert Maillart*, 1949.

BROCK, E. P. LOFTUS, 'The Roman Bridge over the Trent at South Collingham', *The Builder*, 1885.

BRUNEL, I., *The Life of Isambard Kingdom Brunel*, 1870.

BUCKTON, E. J. & Cuerel, J., 'The New Waterloo Bridge', *Journal Inst. C.E.*, 1943.

BUDGE, E. A. WALLIS, *An Account of the Roman Antiquities in the Museum at Chesters and of Excavations on the Roman Wall*, 1903.

BYNE, ARTHUR, 'The Bridges of Spain', *The Architectural Record*, 1916.

CAESAR, JULIUS, *De Bello Gallico*.

CARY, HENRY (translated by), *Works of Herodotus*, 1886.

CLARK, EDWIN, *The Britannia and Conway Tubular Bridges*, 1850.

CUEREL, J. *See* BUCKTON, E. J.

DARTEIN, F. DE, *Études sur les Ponts en Pierre*, 1909-12.

DEGRAND, E. *Ponts en Maçonnerie*, 1888.

DIEULAFOY, M., *L'Art Antique de la Perse*, 1885.

EMERSON, W. & GROMORT, G., *Old Bridges of France*, 1925.

EMERTON, EPHRAIM, 'Altopascio—A Forgotten Order', *American Historical Review*, 1923.

ENNIS, L. *See* FREEMAN, R.

ESPÉRANDIEU, EMILE, *Le Pont du Gard*, 1934.

FREEMAN, RALPH, 'Sydney Harbour Bridge; Design', *Journal Inst. C.E.*, 1934.

FREEMAN, R. & ENNIS, L., 'Sydney Harbour Bridge; Manufacture & Erection', *Journal Inst. C.E.*, 1934.

FREEMAN, RALPH (JR). *See* SHIRLEY SMITH, H.

FREYSSINET, EUGÈNE, 'Pre-stressed concrete', *Journal Inst. C.E.*, 1950.

FROEHNER, W., *La Colonne Trajane*, 1872.

FUGL-MEYER, H., *Chinese Bridges*, 1937.

GALES, SIR ROBERT, 'The Hardinge Bridge', *Proc. Inst. C.E.*, 1917-18.

GAUTHEY, EMILAND-MARIE, *Traité de la Construction des Ponts*, 1809.

GAUTIER, HUBERT, *Traité des Ponts*, 1714.

GIBB, SIR A., *The Story of Telford*, 1935.

GOLDEN GATE BRIDGE & HIGHWAY DISTRICT, THE, *Golden Gate Bridge*, 1938.

GROMORT, G. *See* EMERSON, W.

GWILT, JOSEPH (translated by), *Ten Books of Architecture of Marcus Vitruvius Pollio*, 1826.

HARVEY, B. L., 'The Restoration of the Breach in the Right Guide Bank of the Hardinge Bridge', *Journal Inst. C.E.*, 1936.

HARVEY, JOHN, *The Gothic World*, 1950.
HENDERSON, CHARLES & COATES, HENRY, *Old Cornish Bridges and Streams*, 1928.
HOME, GORDON, *Old London Bridge*, 1931.
HOOKER, J. D., *Himalayan Journals*, 1854.
HOWORTH, G. E., 'The Construction of the Lower Zambesi Bridge', *Journal Inst. C.E.*, 1937.
HOWORTH, G. E. & SHIRLEY SMITH, H., 'The New Howrah Bridge, Calcutta; Construction', *Journal Inst. C.E.*, 1946-7.
INSTITUTION OF CIVIL ENGINEERS, *Report on Regulations for work carried out under Compressed Air*, 1936.
JAKKULA, A. A., *A History of Suspension Bridges*, 1941.
JUSSERAND, J. J., *English Wayfaring Life in the Middle Ages*, 1905.
KNIGHT, WILLIAM, 'The Construction of Old London Bridge', *Archaeologia*, 1831.
LABELYE, CHARLES, *A Description of Westminster Bridge*, 1751.
LANCIANI, RODOLFO, *The Ruins & Excavations of Ancient Rome*, 1897.
LEGER, A., *Les Travaux Publics, les Mines et la Métallurgie aux Temps des Romains*, 1875.
LENTHÉRIC, CHARLES, *Le Rhône, Histoire d'un Fleuve*, Vol. 2, 1892
MAUNSELL, G. A. & PAIN, J. F., 'The Storstrøm Bridge', *Journal Inst. C.E.* 1939.
MIDDLETON, J. H., *The Remains of Ancient Rome*, 1892.
PAIN, J. F. *See* MAUNSELL, G. A.,
PARSONS, WILLIAM BARCLAY, *Engineers and Engineering in the Renaissance*, 1939.
PERRONET, M., *Oeuvres*, 1882-83.
POPE, ARTHUR UPHAM (editor), *A Survey of Persian Art*, 1939.
PORT OF NEW YORK AUTHORITY, *George Washington Bridge*, 1933.
SHIRLEY SMITH, H. & FREEMAN, RALPH (JR), 'The Design & Erection of the Birchenough and Otto Beit Bridges, Rhodesia', *Journal Inst. C.E.*, 1945. *See* also HOWORTH, G. E.
SMILES, SAMUEL, *Lives of the Engineers*, 1874.
SPRING, SIR FRANCIS, *India River Training and Control*, Simla, 1903.
TOWNSEND, RICHARD, *Bridge over the River Serchio near Lucca*, M.S. Inst. C.E., 1842.
VIOLLET-LE-DUC, M., *Dictionnaire Raisonné de l'Architecture*, 1864.
WADDELL, J. A., *Bridge Engineering*, 1916.
WARD, A. M. & BATESON, E., 'The New Howrah Bridge, Calcutta; Design', *Journal Inst. C.E.*, 1946-47.
WESTHOFEN, W., *The Forth Bridge*, reprinted from *Engineering*, 1890.
WIGRAM, E. T. A., *Northern Spain*, 1906.
WOODWARD, C. M., *St. Louis Bridge*, 1881.

ANNUAL REPORTS, *San Francisco–Oakland Bay Bridge*, 1934-39.
REPORTS, ETC., *East River Bridge, New York*, 1869-78.
    Quebec Bridge Enquiry & Report, 1908.
    The Quebec Bridge, Report, 1918.
REPORT OF BOARD OF ENGINEERS, *The Failure of the Tacoma Narrows Bridge*, 1941.
REPORT OF COURT OF ENQUIRY, *Tay Bridge Disaster*, 1880.

Index